REVISE D1

for MEI Structured Mathematics

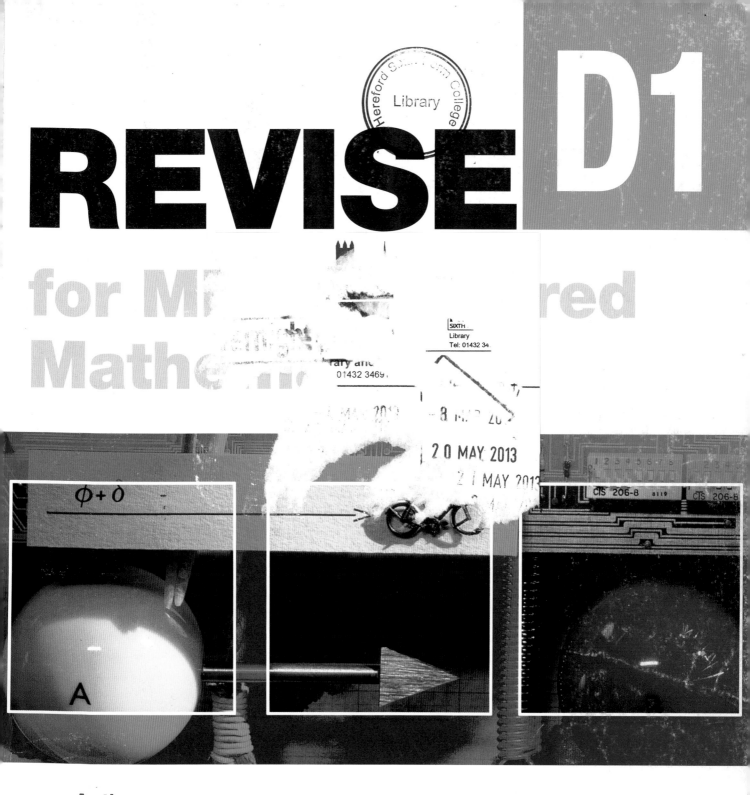

Author
Sue de Pomerai

Editor
Stella Dudzic

Series Editor
Roger Porkess

HODDER
EDUCATION
AN HACHETTE UK COMPANY

Every effort has been made to trace all copyright holders, but if any have been inadvertently overlooked the Publishers will be pleased to make the necessary arrangements at the first opportunity.

Although every effort has been made to ensure that website addresses are correct at time of going to press, Hodder Education cannot be held responsible for the content of any website mentioned in this book. It is sometimes possible to find a relocated web page by typing in the address of the home page for a website in the URL window of your browser.

Hachette UK's policy is to use papers that are natural, renewable and recyclable products and made from wood grown in sustainable forests. The logging and manufacturing processes are expected to conform to the environmental regulations of the country of origin.

Orders: please contact Bookpoint Ltd, 130 Milton Park, Abingdon, Oxon OX14 4SB.
Telephone: (44) 01235 827720. Fax: (44) 01235 400454. Lines are open 9.00 – 5.00, Monday to Saturday, with a 24-hour message answering service.
Visit our website at www.hoddereducation.co.uk

© Sue de Pomerai, Stella Dudzic, 2010
First published in 2010 by
Hodder Education,
An Hachette UK Company
338 Euston Road
London NW1 3BH

Impression number   5 4 3 2 1
Year   2013 2012 2011 2010

Dynamic Learning Student Online website © Sue de Pomerai, Stella Dudzic, Roger Porkess, 2010; with contributions from Louisa Mousley; developed by Infuze Limited and MMT Limited; cast: Tom Frankland; recorded at Alchemy Soho.

Typeset in 11/12 Helvetica by Tech-Set Ltd., Gateshead, Tyne & Wear
Printed in India

A catalogue record for this title is available from the British Library

ISBN: 978 0 340 957370

Contents

Introduction

Welcome to this Revision Guide for the MEI Decision 1 unit!

The book is organised into 11 sections covering the various topics in the syllabus. A typical section is six pages long; the first four pages contain essential information and key worked examples covering the topic. At the start of each chapter, there are page references to where the section topics are covered in the textbook.

The last page in each section has questions for you to answer so that you can be sure that you have really understood the topic. There is a multiple-choice exercise and an exam-style question. If you are to gain the greatest possible benefit from the book, and so do your best in the D1 exam, you should work through these for yourself and then refer to the accompanying website to check your answers.

The multiple-choice questions cover the basic ideas and techniques. It is really important that you work through them carefully; guessing will do you no good at all. When you have decided on the answer you think is right, enter it on the website. If you are right, it tells you so and gives the full solution; check that your answer wasn't just a fluke. If your choice is not right, the website gives you advice about your mistake; the possible wrong answers have all been designed to pick out particular common misunderstandings. The explanations on the website are based on the most likely mistakes; even if you make a different mistake, you will usually find enough help to set you on the right path so that you can try again.

When you come onto the exam-style question, write out your best possible answer. Then go to the website. You will find the solution displayed step-by-step, together with someone talking you through it and giving you helpful advice.

So the book contains the essential information to revise for the exam and, critically, also enables you to check that you have understood it properly. That is a recipe for success.

Finally, a word of warning. This book is designed to be used together with the textbook and not as a replacement for it. This Revision Guide will help you to prepare for the exam but to do really well you also need the deep understanding that comes from the detailed explanations you will find in the textbook.

Good learning and good luck!

Sue de Pomerai, Stella Dudzic, Roger Porkess

Where you see the following icon ⋑L, please refer to the Dynamic Learning Student Online website. Information on how to access this website is printed on the inside front cover of the book.

Accompanying books
MEI Structured Mathematics D1
ISBN 978 0 340 81401 7

Companion to Advanced Mathematics and Statistics
ISBN 978 0 340 95923 7

Algorithms

Definitions and communication

A ABOUT THIS TOPIC

This topic looks at ways in which you can understand and apply algorithms presented in a variety of forms. You will use algorithms in the whole of D1.

R REMEMBER

- No prior knowledge is needed for this chapter.

K KEY FACTS

- An algorithm is a systematic process for solving problems.

- It consists of a set of input data and a list of instructions.

- To solve the problem you take the input and apply the instructions, one at a time, until a solution is reached.

- An algorithm must have the following properties:
  1 **Precision:** each step must be clearly defined.
  2 **Generality:** the algorithm must work for any set of inputs.
  3 **Finiteness:** the algorithm must stop after a finite number of steps when the solution is reached. This means it will need a stopping condition.

Communicating an algorithm

Algorithms can be communicated in various ways, usually as one of the following:

1 a series of steps
2 a flowchart
3 a computer programming language or pseudocode (a mixture of English and computer programming language).

Algorithms often have loops where the process is repeated until the solution is found. These are called **iterations**; each time you go round the loop is one iteration. Because of this, every algorithm must have a **stopping condition** otherwise it would carry on going round the loop forever!

EXAMPLE 1

Complete the table to show the output of the algorithm.
What does the algorithm produce?

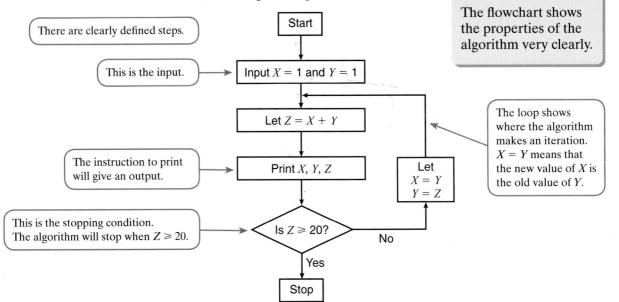

There are clearly defined steps.

This is the input.

The instruction to print will give an output.

This is the stopping condition. The algorithm will stop when $Z \geqslant 20$.

A ADVICE

The flowchart shows the properties of the algorithm very clearly.

The loop shows where the algorithm makes an iteration. $X = Y$ means that the new value of X is the old value of Y.

SOLUTION

Note: The old Y becomes the new X and the old Z becomes the new Y.

X	Y	Z
1	1	2
1	2	3
2	3	5
3	5	8
5	8	13
8	13	21

The instruction is to print X, Y and Z so the output will be all the values of X, Y and Z produced by the algorithm until it stops.

The algorithm produces terms of the Fibonacci sequence.

EXAMPLE 2

Write the algorithm shown in the flowchart as a series of steps.

SOLUTION

Step 1 Let $X = 1$ and $Y = 1$
Step 2 Let $Z = X + Y$
Step 3 Print X, Y and Z
Step 4 If $Z \geqslant 20$ go to step 8
Step 5 If $Z < 20$ go to step 6
Step 6 Let $X = Y$ and let $Y = Z$
Step 7 Go to step 2
Step 8 Stop

A ADVICE

In the exam you may well be asked to work through an algorithm which you have never seen before expressed as a list of instructions or in a flowchart.

Types of algorithm

All algorithms are designed to find the **optimal solution**; that is, the best possible answer to a problem.

A heuristic algorithm is one which provides a solution but does not necessarily guarantee that this is an optimal solution.

A greedy algorithm is one that makes the best choice at each stage with the hope of finding the optimal solution. The choice made by a greedy algorithm may depend on choices made so far but not consider future choices. Greedy algorithms produce good solutions to some optimisation problems but they do not necessarily find the optimal solution. Several of the network algorithms in chapter 3 are greedy algorithms.

Bin packing

These are methods for fitting things into a limited amount of space. This first method is a strategy rather than an algorithm because each step is not clearly defined.

Full bin: Look for combinations that will fill one bin, then any remaining items are grouped together so that there is as little space wasted as possible. This can be very efficient if there is a small amount of data.

EXAMPLE 3	Use the full bin method to pack the following weights, in kg, into boxes that can hold 8 kg each.
	$2, 4, 6, 3, 3, 2, 5, 6$

A ADVICE

You may find it helpful to cross the weights off the list once you have included them in the solution.

SOLUTION		
Box 1	6, 2	You will quickly notice that $6 + 2 = 8, 6 + 2 = 8, 5 + 3 = 8$ leaving 4 and 3 in the final box.
Box 2	6, 2	
Box 3	5, 3	
Box 4	4, 3	

The disadvantages of this method are that if there is a large number of items, or if there are no full bin combinations, then it is very difficult to apply.

There are two heuristic algorithms that are easier to apply to large numbers of inputs.

First-fit: Using the items in the order they are given, place each item in the first bin that has enough space. This algorithm is easy to apply but does not often give an efficient solution. This can be seen in the next example.

EXAMPLE 4

Use the first-fit method to pack the following weights, in kg, into boxes that can hold 8 kg each.

$$2, 4, 6, 3, 3, 2, 5, 6$$

SOLUTION

Box 1   2, 4, 2

Box 2   6

Box 3   3, 3

Box 4   5

Box 5   6

> The 6 will not fit in box 1 so it goes into box 2.

First-fit decreasing: This algorithm re-orders the items in descending order before it packs them. By fitting in the larger items first it usually finds a more efficient solution if one is available.

Put the items in order of size from the largest to the smallest then follow the pattern of the first-fit algorithm.

 Although the first-fit decreasing algorithm is often more efficient, you should not assume that it will automatically give a better solution. There are many problems where this is not the case.

EXAMPLE 5

Use the first-fit decreasing method to pack the weights in Example 4 into boxes that can hold 8 kg each.

SOLUTION

Rewrite the items in order of size from the largest to the smallest.

$$6, 6, 5, 4, 3, 3, 2, 2$$

Box 1   6, 2

Box 2   6, 2

Box 3   5, 3

Box 4   4, 3

> This table shows which box each of the weights has been put in and the order in which it happened.

Weight	6	6	5	4	3	3	2	2
Box	1	2	3	4	3	4	1	2

LINKS

Decision Mathematics	Understanding algorithms is essential for the rest of the D1 module. You will meet more algorithms if you study D2 or DC.
Pure Mathematics	You will learn several iterative algorithms for solving equations in C3.
Numerical Methods	Iterative Algorithms for Numerical Solution of Equations, Differentiation and Integration.

Test Yourself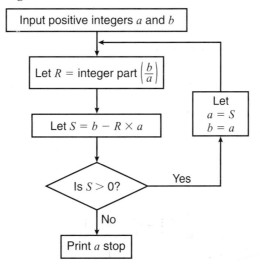

Questions 1 to 3 are about the algorithm shown in this flowchart.

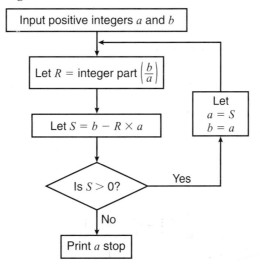

Input positive integers a and b

Let R = integer part $\left(\dfrac{b}{a}\right)$

Let $S = b - R \times a$

Is $S > 0$?

Let $a = S$ $b = a$

Yes

No

Print a stop

1 If you run the algorithm with $a = 105$ and $b = 180$, what is the printed output?

A $75, 30, 15, 0$ B $105, 75, 30, 15$

C 15 D 105

2 One of the statements below is correct. Pick the correct statement.

A The algorithm finds multiples of 15.

B The algorithm finds the remainder when b is divided by a.

C The algorithm finds the highest common factor of 105 and 180.

D The algorithm finds the highest common factor of a and b.

Make sure you have the correct answer to question 1 before doing question 3.

3 If you run the algorithm with $a = 180$ and $b = 105$, one of the statements below is correct. Pick the correct statement.

A You get the same answer in the same number of iterations.

B You get the same answer but it takes one extra iteration.

C It is not possible to get an answer because a is bigger than b.

D The answer is 180.

4 A warehouse has storage racks that are 1.8 m high. Nine containers need to be stored. Their heights (in cm) are 90, 25, 105, 100, 80, 50, 70, 80, 120. Three maths students, working during their holidays, try to calculate how many racks will be needed using full bin, first-fit and first-fit decreasing algorithms. Which one of the following statements is true?

A The first-fit decreasing method uses fewer racks than the first-fit or full bin.

B The three methods all use the same number of racks.

C The first-fit decreasing method uses six racks.

D It is not possible to use the full bin method as there are only two full bins.

Exam-Style Question

The flowchart below defines an algorithm with input a, where a is a positive integer.

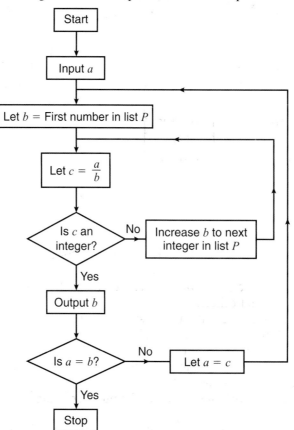

List P, which is referred to in the flowchart, is the list of prime numbers $2, 3, 5, 7, 11, 13, 17, ...$
i)   Run the algorithm with input $a = 90$.
ii)   Say what the algorithm achieves.
iii)   What is the final value of c for **any** initial value of a? Explain your answer.

Sorting algorithms

A ABOUT THIS TOPIC

This topic looks at some algorithms for sorting lists of numbers. It introduces the idea of comparing the efficiency of two algorithms and goes on to discuss basic ideas of complexity of algorithms.

These ideas have become important with the rapid development of computer technology.

R REMEMBER

- You need to remember what the properties of an algorithm are and how algorithms are communicated.

K KEY FACTS

- You are *not* expected to remember the sorting algorithms for the exam but you must be able to follow the algorithm presented in any of the ways given in the previous section. The sorting algorithms you could meet include *bubble sort, quick sort, interchange sort, insertion sort* and *shuttle sort*, but you may meet others.
- Some algorithms are more efficient than others; they may need fewer operations or take less processing time to reach the solution to a problem. The *complexity* of an algorithm is the maximum number of operations needed to solve the problem.
- You can compare the efficiency of sorting algorithms by looking at the number of comparisons and swaps they need to complete the sort.
- If an algorithm has *linear complexity*, doubling the number of inputs will double the time taken to run the algorithm.
- If an algorithm has *quadratic complexity*, doubling the number of inputs will increase the time taken by a factor of 4 because $2^2 = 4$.
- If an algorithm has *cubic complexity*, doubling the number of inputs will increase the time taken by a factor of 8 because $2^3 = 8$.

Algorithms for sorting

These are some of the sorts you may meet in the exam.

- **Bubble sort**, which compares every pair of numbers in the list, swapping where necessary. At each pass this sort fixes numbers in their correct position from the bottom of the list (see Example 2).
- **Quick sort**, which splits the items into smaller and smaller sublists by selecting a *pivot* element in each sublist then sorting the sublists into items greater than and those less than the pivot (see Example 5).
- **Interchange sort** finds the smallest number in the list and swaps it with the first number in the list. It then finds the next smallest number and swaps it with the second number in the list. It carries on doing this until the list is sorted (see Example 1).
- **Insertion sort** takes the numbers one at a time from the list and inserts them into the correct position.
- **Shuttle sort** starts by comparing the first two numbers and swapping if necessary, then compares the second and third numbers, swaps if necessary and, if they have swapped, then compares the new second number with the first number and swaps if necessary etc. (see Example 6).

In sorting, each iteration is called a **pass**.

EXAMPLE 1

Use the interchange sort to sort this list of numbers in ascending order: 17, 9, 2, 27, 4, 15. Record the number of comparisons and swaps made.

SOLUTION

The first pass picks 2 as the smallest in the list and swaps it with 17; you do not consider the 2 again.

The second pass picks 4 as the smallest number in the remaining list and swaps it with 9; you do not consider the 4 again.

Pass	1	2	3	4	5	
17	2	2	2	2	2	
9	9	4	4	4	4	
2	17	17	9	9	9	
27	27	27	27	15	15	
4	4	9	17	17	17	
15	15	15	15	27	27	**Totals**
Comparisons	5	4	3	2	1	**15**
Exchanges	1	1	1	1		**4**

The algorithm continues in this way until the sort is complete.

Work out the number of comparisons.

The list has six numbers. The algorithm compares pairs of numbers to find the smallest like this.

Compare 17 with 9; 9 is smaller.
Compare 9 with 2; 2 is smaller.
Compare 2 with 27; 2 is smaller.
Compare 2 with 4; 2 is smaller.
Compare 2 with 15; 2 is smaller.

This is five comparisons in total.

> **Note:** There are five comparisons for a list of six numbers.
> In general there will always be one less comparison than there are numbers in the list.

Note that it does not matter whether you set out the passes vertically, as in Example 1, or horizontally like this.

List: 17, 9, 2, 27, 4, 15
First pass   2, 9, 17, 27, 4, 15
Second pass   2, 4, 17, 27, 9, 15, ..., etc.

Bubble sort

Step 1:   Compare the first two numbers.

Step 2:   If the second number is smaller than the first, exchange the numbers.

Step 3:   Compare the second number with the next number.

Step 4:   Repeat steps 2 and 3 for all pairs of numbers until you reach the end of the list.

Step 5:   Repeat steps 1 to 4 until no more exchanges are made.

EXAMPLE 2

Use the bubble sort to sort this list of numbers in ascending order: 17, 9, 2, 27, 4, 15. Record the number of comparisons and swaps made.

SOLUTION

This table shows every step in the first pass.

Compare 17 and 9 Swap	Compare 17 and 2 Swap	Compare 17 and 27 Don't swap	Compare 27 and 4 Swap	Compare 27 and 15 Swap	27 is now fixed as the largest number in the list
17	9	9	9	9	9
9	17	2	2	2	2
2	2	17	17	17	17
27	27	27	27	4	4
4	4	4	4	27	15
15	15	15	15	15	27

> You do not need to show passes in this much detail in an exam. You will not have time to show much working.

	Pass				
	1	**2**	**3**	**4**	
	17	9	2	2	2
	9	2	9	4	4
	2	17	4	9	9
	27	4	15	15	15
	4	15	17	17	17
	15	27	27	27	27
Comparisons	5	4	3	2	**Totals**
Exchanges	4	3	1	0	14
					8

A ADVICE

Advice: On the first pass, the first number in the list is compared with the second and if the second number is smaller they swap places. The second number is then compared with the third and the smaller is placed in the second position, and so on. At the end of the first pass, the largest number will be at the bottom. For the list of six numbers in this example, this involves five comparisons and four swaps. After the first pass the bottom number is fixed in its final position in the list.

Second pass: Repeat first pass but don't consider the last number (on the third pass the last two numbers are excluded and so on).

Continue in this way until **no swaps take place in a pass**; this is the stopping condition for the bubble sort.

EXAMPLE 3

What is the maximum number of passes needed to sort a list of n numbers using the bubble sort?

SOLUTION

After one pass the biggest number is fixed at the bottom so there are only $n - 1$ numbers left to sort. After two passes there are $n - 2$ numbers left to sort and so on. After $n - 1$ passes there is only 1 number left and you don't need to sort 1 number.

So, if you start with a list of n numbers, the list will definitely be sorted after the $(n - 1)^{\text{th}}$ pass. This is the maximum number of passes.

EXAMPLE 4

i) What is the maximum number of comparisons and swaps needed to sort a list of six numbers using the bubble sort?

ii) Generalise this for a list of n numbers.

SOLUTION

i) Example 2 shows five comparisons on the first pass. There is one number fewer on the second pass so only four comparisons are needed. And so on; so for a list of six numbers, the maximum number of comparisons needed is $5 + 4 + 3 + 2 + 1 = 15$.

Each comparison could result in a swap so the maximum number of swaps is the same as the maximum number of comparisons; it is also 15.

ii) For a list of n numbers the maximum number of comparisons needed is $(n - 1) + (n - 2) + \ldots + 2 + 1$ and the number of swaps is also $(n - 1) + (n - 2) + \ldots + 2 + 1$.

Quick sort

Step 1: Select a pivot element x from the list L – usually the first number in the list.

Step 2: Split the list into two sub-lists, L_1 containing all the numbers less than or equal to x and L_2 containing all the numbers greater than x.

Step 3 : Write the L_1 above x and L_2 below x (x is now fixed in its correct place in the list).

Step 4: Apply steps 1 to 3 to each separate list with more than one number until all of the lists contain only one number.

Step 5: Stop, the original list is now in ascending order.

EXAMPLE 5

Use the quick sort to sort this list of numbers in ascending order: 17, 9, 2, 27, 4, 15. Record the number of comparisons made.

SOLUTION

The first pivot is 17.

All the other numbers are compared to 17 and are placed above it if they are smaller or below it if they are larger. This is the result at the end of the first pass.

Pass	1	2	3	
17	9	2	2	
9	2	4	4	
2	4	9	9	
27	15	15	15	
4	17	17	17	
15	27	27	27	**Totals**
Comparisons	5	3	1	9

Shuttle sort

Step 1: Compare the first two numbers and exchange if necessary.

Step 2: Compare the second and third numbers and exchange if necessary, then compare the second and first numbers and exchange if necessary.

Step 3: Compare the third and fourth numbers and exchange if necessary, compare the second and third numbers and exchange if necessary, compare the second and first numbers and exchange if necessary.

Step 4: For a list of length n, continue until $n - 1$ passes have been performed.

EXAMPLE 6

Use the shuttle sort to sort this list of numbers in ascending order: 17, 9, 2, 27, 4, 15. Record the number of comparisons made.

SOLUTION

Pass	1	2	3	4	5	
17	9	2	2	2	2	
9	17	9	9	4	4	
2	2	17	17	9	9	
27	27	27	27	17	15	
4	4	4	4	27	17	
15	15	15	15	15	27	**Total**
Comparisons	1	2	3	4	5	15
Swaps	1	2	0	3	2	8

> Start the algorithm by comparing the 17 and 9.

> At the end of the first pass you swap the 17 and 9 since 17 > 9.

Note: Unlike the bubble sort, the shuttle sort starts by only comparing the first two numbers, then the first three numbers and so on. Since this is the case, for a list of n numbers it will always need $n - 1$ passes.

Efficiency of an algorithm

Questions often ask about the relative efficiency of sorting algorithms by comparing the number of comparisons and swaps that are made to sort the same list of numbers.

EXAMPLE 7

When sorting the list of numbers 17, 9, 2, 27, 4, 15, which algorithm is more efficient, the bubble sort or the shuttle sort?

SOLUTION

In Example 2, the bubble sort has 14 comparisons and 8 swaps.
In Example 6, the shuttle sort has 15 comparisons and 8 swaps. The total number of comparisons and swaps is fewer for the bubble sort than for the shuttle sort, so the bubble sort is more efficient for this list.

Complexity of an algorithm

The complexity of an algorithm is a measure of how efficient the algorithm is. It is sometimes called the *order* of the algorithm. Algorithms can have linear complexity (order 1), quadratic complexity (order 2), cubic complexity (order 3) or more. An algorithm with linear complexity will take twice as long to run if you double the number of inputs. An algorithm with quadratic complexity will take 2^2 times as long to run if you double the number of inputs and so on.

EXAMPLE 8

An algorithm has order 2. If the input is 500 pieces of data, it takes 3 seconds to run the algorithm.
How long would it take to run the algorithm if the input was 2000 pieces of data?

A ADVICE

Order 2 means it has quadratic complexity so if four times as much data is input, you must multiply the time taken by four squared.

SOLUTION $2000 = 500 \times 4$ so the amount of data is four times as big.

Time taken $= 3 \times 4^2 = 3 \times 16 = 48$ seconds.

So far all the examples in this section have sorted the list in ascending order. To sort a list in descending order use the same ideas but put smaller numbers lower in the list. Example 9 uses the bubble sort to sort a list in descending order.

EXAMPLE 9   Use the bubble sort to sort this list of numbers in descending order: 17, 9, 2, 27, 4, 15. Record the number of comparisons and swaps made.

SOLUTION

Pass	1	2	3	4	
17	17	17	27	27	
9	9	27	17	17	
2	27	9	15	15	
27	4	15	9	9	
4	15	4	4	4	
15	2	2	2	2	**Totals**
Comparisons	5	4	3	2	14
Exchanges	3	2	2	0	7

LINKS

Understanding algorithms is essential for the rest of the D1 module. You will meet more algorithms if you study D2 or DC.

Test Yourself

Questions 1 to 3 are about this list of numbers: 52, 48, 50, 45, 64, 47, 53

1 How many passes does it take to sort the list in ascending order using the bubble sort?

A 20   B 6   C 5   D 4

2 Look at the algorithm for the shuttle sort in Example 6.
If you use this algorithm to sort the list of numbers above in ascending order, what is the result after the third pass?

A 45, 48, 50, 52, 64, 47, 53   B 48, 50, 45, 52, 64, 47, 53

C 52, 50, 48, 45, 64, 47, 53   D 52, 48, 50, 45, 47, 53, 64

3 Sort the list in descending order using the interchange sort. What is the result at the end of the third pass?

A 45, 47, 48, 52, 64, 50, 53   B 64, 53, 52, 45, 50, 47, 48

C 45, 47, 48, 52, 50, 64, 53   D 64, 53, 52, 48, 50, 45, 47

4 An algorithm has cubic complexity. If it takes 10 seconds to process 600 pieces of data, how long would it take to process 1800 pieces of data?

A 30 seconds   B 1000 seconds   C 270 seconds   D 27 000 seconds

Exam-Style Question ⋙

Bubble sort

Step 1: Compare the first two numbers.

Step 2: If the second number is larger than the first, exchange the numbers.

Step 3: Compare the second number with the next number.

Step 4: Repeat steps 2 and 3 for all pairs of numbers until you reach the end of the list.

Step 5: Repeat steps 1 to 4 until no more exchanges are made.

In a test, Ali scores 57, Bob scores 67, Cath scores 48, Donna scores 72 and Ewan scores 62.

i) Use a bubble sort to rearrange the individuals from alphabetic order into descending order of merit. Show the list of scores after each pass of the algorithm.

ii) How many comparisons and swaps were made in performing the bubble sort?

iii) Fiona takes the test late and scores 60. Her score is inserted into the list by comparing it with the best score, then with the second best, etc., until it can be put in the correct place. How many comparisons were made in total performing the bubble sort and then inserting Fiona's score into the list?

iv) How many comparisons would have been made using the bubble sort if Fiona's score had been available in the first place, and she had been listed after Ewan? Comment on the result.

Graphs

Graph theory

▸▸ 43

A ABOUT THIS TOPIC

This section deals with the notation and terminology of graph theory and how graphs can be used to model certain types of problems. Famous historical problems which have been solved using graphs include the Konigsberg bridges and the four colour problem.

R REMEMBER

- No prior knowledge is needed for this chapter.

K KEY FACTS

Terminology for graph theory

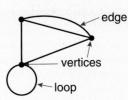

- **Vertex/node** – the dots in a graph (usually where two, or more, edges meet, but not necessarily).
- **Edge/arc** – a line between two vertices.
- **Graph** – collection of vertices (or nodes) and edges (or arcs).
- **Simple graph** –a graph with no loops and no more than one edge between any pair of vertices.
- **Connected graph** – a graph in which there is a route from each vertex to any other vertex (i.e. the graph is in one part).
- **Planar graph** – one which can be drawn with no edges crossing.
- **Complete graph** – A simple graph in which every pair of vertices is connected by an edge.
- **Subgraph** – any set of edges and vertices taken from a graph is a subgraph.
- **Digraph** – a graph in which there is at least one directed edge.
- **Bipartite graph** – one in which the vertices are in two sets and each edge connects a vertex from each set.
- **Path** – a route from one vertex to another which does not repeat any vertex.
- **Walk** – a sequence of edges in which the end of one edge is the beginning of the next. You can visit a vertex more than once and you can traverse an edge more than once too.
- **Trail** – a walk with no repeated edges, though you can visit a vertex more than once.
- **Cycle** – a route starting and finishing at the same vertex.
- **Tree** – a connected graph with no cycles.
- **Spanning tree** – a subgraph that includes all the vertices of the original graph and is also a tree.
- **Degree (or order) of a vertex** – the number of edges starting or finishing at that vertex.
- **Hamilton (or Hamiltonian) cycle** – a cycle that visits every vertex of the graph exactly once.
- **Euler (or Eulerian) cycle** – a cycle that travels along every edge of the graph.
- **Eulerian graph** – a graph with no odd vertices. An Eulerian graph is traversable.
- **Incidence matrix** – a matrix showing the number of edges between each pair of vertices in a graph.

Graphs can be used to represent many different things.

This graph represents a cuboid.

The 8 vertices of the graph represent the 8 vertices (or corners) of the cuboid.

The 12 edges of the graph represent the 12 edges of the cuboid.

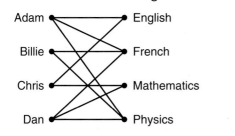

This **bipartite graph** shows which subjects four students study.

A ADVICE

Questions on graphs can cover a variety of ideas so it is very important that you know and understand all the vocabulary for graph theory.

EXAMPLE 1

The diagram represents the two floors of a house.

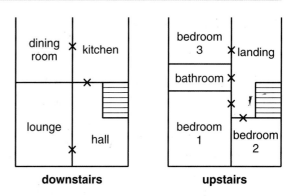

There are seven rooms plus a hall and a landing, which can be considered as separate rooms. Each × represents a doorway connecting two rooms. The ≡ represents the staircase, connecting the hall and the landing. Draw a graph to represent this information, with vertices representing rooms, and edges representing connections between rooms.

What type of graph is this an example of?

SOLUTION

This graph is a tree since it has no cycles.

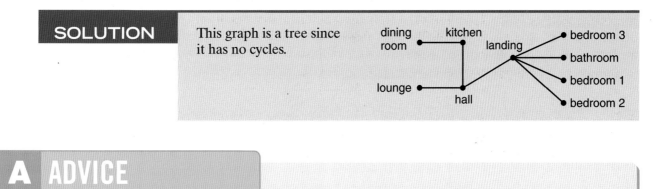

A ADVICE

Represent each room and the hall and landing by a vertex; nine vertices altogether.

Join the rooms where there are doors. The hall is joined to the landing by an edge which represents the staircase.

EXAMPLE 2

The table shows the number of vertices of degree 1, 2, 3 and 4 for three different graphs.

Draw an example of each of these graphs.

Degree of vertex	1	2	3	4
Graph A	3	0	1	0
Graph B	0	0	4	1
Graph C	0	2	2	1

SOLUTION

Graph A: notice that the graph has three vertices of degree 1 and one vertex of degree 3.
So there are four vertices altogether.

Start by drawing the four vertices.

Join up the loose ends of the edges.

Then you can tidy it up to get something like this.

Graph B   Graph C

Note: the graphs can look different but still be correct, as long as the vertices have the right degree.

This is also a correct answer for graph B.

EXAMPLE 3

Find the number of edges and the sum of the degrees of the vertices for each graph in Example 2. What do you notice?

SOLUTION

Graph A: number of edges **3**, sum of degrees of vertices $1 + 1 + 1 + 3 = $ **6**
Graph B: number of edges **8**, sum of degrees of vertices $3 + 3 + 3 + 3 + 4 = $ **16**
Graph C: number of edges **7**, sum of degrees of vertices $2 + 2 + 3 + 3 + 4 = $ **14**

The sum of the degrees of the vertices is always twice the number of edges.

Note: this is called the **handshaking theorem** and it is an important result in graph theory.

It can be stated mathematically as $\sum \deg v = 2e$.

From this you can deduce that, since the sum of the degrees of the vertices is always even, there are always an even number of odd vertices in any graph.

You do not need to know the name of this theorem for the exam but it is useful to help you understand traversability and Euler cycles.

Traversability

A traversable graph can be drawn without taking your pen off the paper and without going over any edge twice.

Graphs that have exactly two odd vertices are traversable. You start at one of the odd vertices and finish at the other odd vertex. A graph with exactly two odd vertices is called **semi-Eulerian**.

If you can draw a traversable graph that starts and finishes in the same place then it is also an **Eulerian** graph so all the vertices must be even.

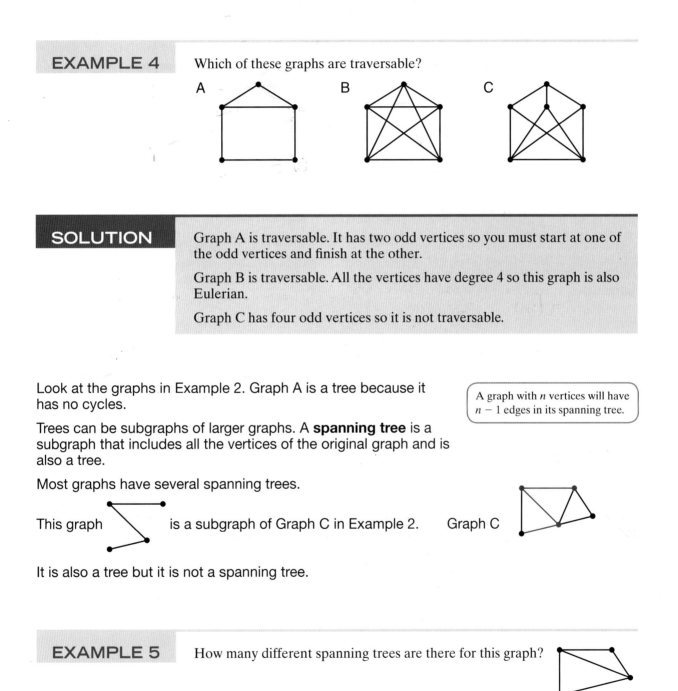

EXAMPLE 4   Which of these graphs are traversable?

A   B   C

SOLUTION   Graph A is traversable. It has two odd vertices so you must start at one of the odd vertices and finish at the other.

Graph B is traversable. All the vertices have degree 4 so this graph is also Eulerian.

Graph C has four odd vertices so it is not traversable.

Look at the graphs in Example 2. Graph A is a tree because it has no cycles.

> A graph with n vertices will have $n-1$ edges in its spanning tree.

Trees can be subgraphs of larger graphs. A **spanning tree** is a subgraph that includes all the vertices of the original graph and is also a tree.

Most graphs have several spanning trees.

This graph   is a subgraph of Graph C in Example 2.   Graph C

It is also a tree but it is not a spanning tree.

EXAMPLE 5   How many different spanning trees are there for this graph?

SOLUTION

There are eight different spanning trees.

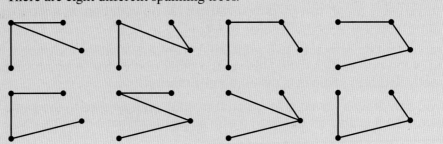

> It is unlikely that you would have to find all the spanning trees of a graph in the exam but, if you do have to draw all the spanning trees, you must take care to work systematically.

Isomorphic graphs

Graphs are isomorphic if one can be stretched or twisted to make the other.

Isomorphic graphs must have the same number of vertices with the same degrees connected in the same way.

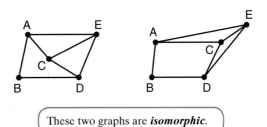

These two graphs are *isomorphic*.

Incidence matrices

A graph can be represented by an incidence matrix that shows how many edges connect pairs of vertices.

EXAMPLE 6   Draw the graph represented by

	A	B	C	D
A	0	2	0	1
B	2	0	1	1
C	0	1	2	0
D	1	1	0	0

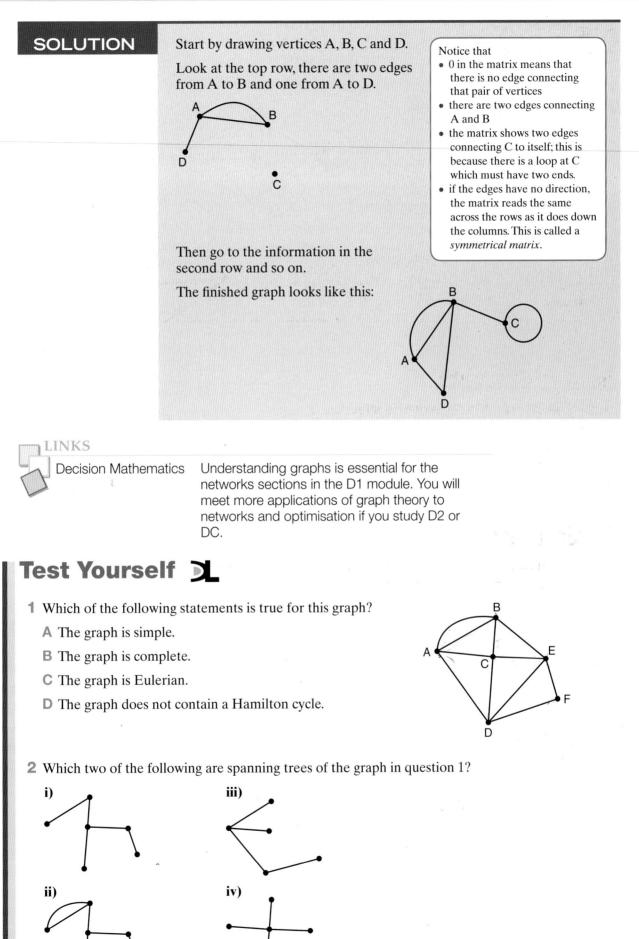

SOLUTION

Start by drawing vertices A, B, C and D.

Look at the top row, there are two edges from A to B and one from A to D.

Then go to the information in the second row and so on.

The finished graph looks like this:

Notice that
- 0 in the matrix means that there is no edge connecting that pair of vertices
- there are two edges connecting A and B
- the matrix shows two edges connecting C to itself; this is because there is a loop at C which must have two ends.
- if the edges have no direction, the matrix reads the same across the rows as it does down the columns. This is called a *symmetrical matrix*.

LINKS

Decision Mathematics — Understanding graphs is essential for the networks sections in the D1 module. You will meet more applications of graph theory to networks and optimisation if you study D2 or DC.

Test Yourself

1 Which of the following statements is true for this graph?

A The graph is simple.

B The graph is complete.

C The graph is Eulerian.

D The graph does not contain a Hamilton cycle.

2 Which two of the following are spanning trees of the graph in question 1?

i)

iii)

ii)

iv)

A **i)** and **ii)**

C **ii)** and **iii)**

B **i)** and **iv)**

D **iii)** and **iv)**

Questions 3 and 4 refer to this graph.

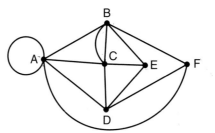

3 Which of the following are Hamilton cycles?

   i) CEBFDAC   **ii)** ABECDA   **iii)** BFADECB   **iv)** AFBDECA

   A **i)** only   B **iii)** only   C **i)** and **iii)**   D **ii)** and **iv)**

   E **i)**, **iii)** and **iv)**

> Remember:
> a Hamiltonian cycle is a cycle that visits every vertex in a graph exactly once and returns to the starting vertex.

4 Which is the incidence matrix for the graph?

A

	A	B	C	D	E	F
A	2	1	1	1	0	1
B	1	0	2	0	1	1
C	1	2	0	1	1	0
D	1	0	1	0	1	1
E	0	1	1	1	0	0
F	1	1	0	1	0	0

B

	A	B	C	D	E	F
A	2	1	1	1	1	1
B	1	0	2	1	1	1
C	1	2	0	1	1	1
D	1	1	1	0	1	1
E	1	1	1	1	0	1
F	1	1	1	1	1	0

C

	A	B	C	D	E	F
A	1	1	1	1	0	1
B	1	0	2	0	1	1
C	1	2	0	1	1	0
D	1	0	1	0	1	1
E	0	1	1	1	0	0
F	1	1	0	1	0	0

D

	A	B	C	D	E	F
A	2	1	1	1	0	1
B	1	0	1	0	1	1
C	1	1	0	1	1	0
D	1	0	1	0	1	1
E	0	1	1	1	0	0
F	1	1	0	1	0	0

5 The graph shown represents the two floors of a building.
Which building does it represent?

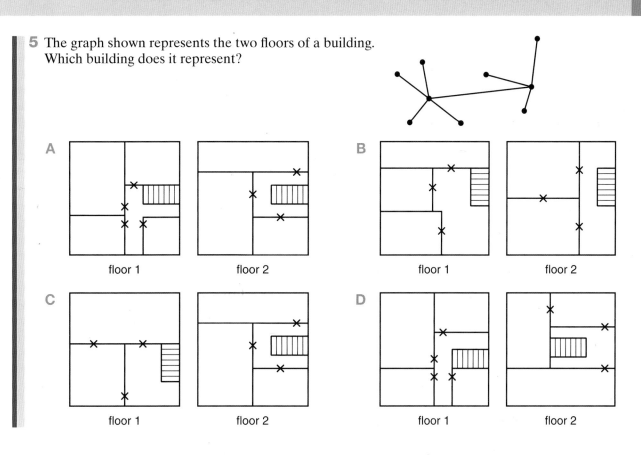

A | floor 1 | floor 2

B | floor 1 | floor 2

C | floor 1 | floor 2

D | floor 1 | floor 2

Exam-Style Question ⋗L

i) A graph has five vertices; two are of degree 4, two are of degree 3 and one is of degree 2.
   Find the number of edges in the graph.

ii) Is the graph Eulerian, semi-Eulerian or neither? Give a reason for your answer.

The graph shows direct bus routes between the homes of three friends,
Amiya, Ben and Carrie.

Di's house can be reached by bus from any of the other houses while Ed's can only be reached from
Ben's or Di's. There is at most one bus route between any pair of houses.

iii) Copy the graph and add the extra edges needed to show all the bus routes.
   How many bus routes are there in total? Is your graph simple? Justify your answer.

iv) Amiya decides to visit Ed. What is the fewest number of buses she must catch?
   How many different ways can she travel to Ed's using this number of buses?

v) An extra bus route is created and Amiya notices that this makes the graph Eulerian.
   Which two friends' houses are connected by the new route?

Networks

Minimum connector

A ABOUT THIS TOPIC

This topic is about finding a spanning tree of minimum length in a network, used in industry for problems where a set of objects or places need to be connected together such as linking a group of towns for a cable TV company or a computer network in a large office.

R REMEMBER

- Some of the vocabulary and ideas introduced in the Graphs chapter.
- Knowledge of how algorithms are communicated and how to follow an algorithm.

K KEY FACTS

- A **network** is a graph with weights (numbers) associated with each edge.

- The weights can stand for a variety of things such as distance, cost or time. The weights are often thought of as lengths.

- The **minimum connector problem** is to find a spanning tree of minimum length in a network.

- You need to learn two algorithms for finding the minimum connector:
  Kruskal's algorithm – at each stage select the shortest unselected edge, provided that a cycle is not formed.
  1 Choose the shortest edge (if there is more than one, choose any of the shortest).
  2 Choose the next shortest edge in the network (it doesn't have to be joined to the edges already connected) and add it.
  3 Choose the next shortest edge which does not create a cycle and add it.
  4 Repeat step 3 until all the vertices are connected then stop.

Prim's algorithm – start at any vertex. At each stage, connect in the vertex which is nearest to any vertex that is already connected.
1 Choose a vertex.
2 Choose the shortest edge from this vertex to any vertex connected directly to it.
3 Look at the vertices that are not already in the solution. Choose the shortest edge from one of these to a vertex that is in the solution. This should not create a cycle.
4 Repeat step 3 until all the vertices are connected then stop.

- You can be asked to find the minimum connector using Prim's algorithm either from a network or from a table.

Kruskal's algorithm

EXAMPLE 1

Find the minimum connector for this network using Kruskal's algorithm.

Show clearly the order in which you connect in the edges.

Draw the minimum connector.

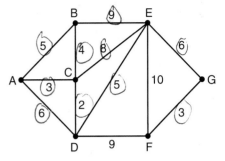

A ADVICE

In questions, the terms *minimum connector* or *minimum spanning tree* may be used. You need to understand that these mean the same thing.

SOLUTION

Edge	Weight	
CD	2	
AC	3	These two edges could
GF	3	be selected in any order
CB	4	
AB	**5**	**Do NOT include AB**
DE	5	**as it makes a cycle**
EG	6	
Total weight	23	

Choose the shortest edge, in this case CD.
Choose the next shortest edge in the network and add it; this is either AC or GF (remember: it doesn't have to be joined to the edges already connected).
Choose the next shortest edge which does not create a cycle and add it.
Repeat until all the vertices are connected.

Order of connecting the edges	Weight	In MST?
CD	2	y
AC	3	y
GF	3	y
CB	4	y
DE	5	y
EG	6	y

Weight of minimum connector
2 + 3 + 3 + 4 + 5 + 6 = 23

Minimum connector (minimum spanning tree)

Notice that AB is not included as this would make a cycle.

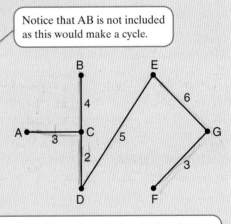

Notice that the number of edges in the minimum connector is always one less than the number of vertices in the network.

A ADVICE

It can be easier to list the edges in ascending order of length before choosing the edges that will be in the minimum connector.

Prim's algorithm

EXAMPLE 2

Find the minimum connector for this network using Prim's algorithm, starting at vertex A.

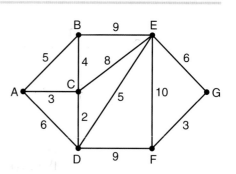

SOLUTION

You are told to start at vertex A. A•

Choose the shortest edge from this vertex to any vertex connected directly to it – this is vertex C.

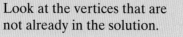

Look at the vertices that are not already in the solution.

Choose the shortest edge from one of these to a vertex that is in the solution. This should not create a cycle.

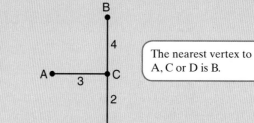

Look at the vertices that are not already in the solution.

Repeat until all the vertices are connected.

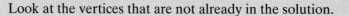

The nearest vertex to A, C or D is B.

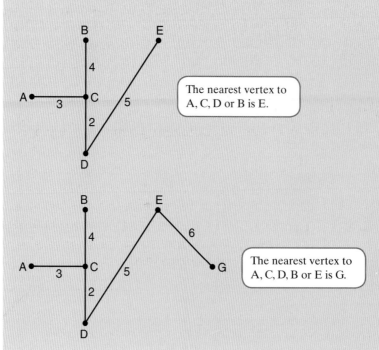

The nearest vertex to A, C, D or B is E.

The nearest vertex to A, C, D, B or E is G.

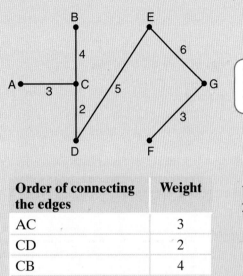

The only vertex not now connected is F.
F is nearest to vertex G .
This is the minimum connector.

Order of connecting the edges	Weight
AC	3
CD	2
CB	4
DE	5
EG	6
GF	3

Weight of minimum connector
$2 + 3 + 3 + 4 + 5 + 6 = 23$

In this example you started at vertex A but this is not always the case. In the exam you will be told which vertex to start at so read the question carefully and be sure to start at the right vertex.

A ADVICE

Notice that the two algorithms give the same answer but the edges have been connected in a different order. The examiner needs to see the order in which you have connected the edges to be certain that you have used the right algorithm so make sure you show this in your solution.

Prim's algorithm on a table

You need to know how to use Prim's algorithm from a matrix or table as well as on a network.

EXAMPLE 3

Use the matrix form of Prim's algorithm, starting at A, to find the minimum spanning tree for the network defined by this table. Draw the minimum spanning tree and give its weight.

SOLUTION

Prim's algorithm on a matrix (table)

1 Choose a column, mark it and cross out its row. Here A has been chosen. Delete row A.
2 Choose the smallest number in the column and circle it. If there is a choice, choose either.
3 For the number you have just circled, cross out its row and put a mark above its column at the top of the table.
4 Choose the smallest number not already crossed out from the marked columns and circle it.
5 Repeat steps 3 and 4 until all the vertices have been included in the tree.

The circled numbers give the edges in the minimum spanning tree.

	A	B	C	D	E	F	G
A	–	5	3	6	–	–	–
B	5	–	4	–	9	–	–
C	3	4	–	2	8	–	–
D	6	–	2	–	5	9	–
E	–	9	8	5	–	10	6
F	–	–	–	9	10	–	3
G	–	–	–	–	6	3	–

Explaining the table
The 5 in row A and column B means the edge from A to B has weight 5. A dash means there is no direct connection.

Start by labelling vertex A as number 1 and crossing out row A as you will not want to include A again. Look for the smallest entry in column A which is 3 at AC.

1

	A	B	C	D	E	F	G
~~A~~	~~–~~	~~5~~	~~3~~	~~6~~	~~–~~	~~–~~	~~–~~
B	5	–	4	–	9	–	–
C	③	4	–	2	8	–	–
D	6	–	2	–	5	9	–
E	–	9	8	5	–	10	6
F	–	–	–	9	10	–	3
G	–	–	–	–	6	3	–

1   2

	A	B	C	D	E	F	G
~~A~~	~~–~~	~~5~~	~~3~~	~~6~~	~~–~~	~~–~~	~~–~~
B	5	–	4	–	9	–	–
~~C~~	~~③~~	~~4~~	~~–~~	~~2~~	~~8~~	~~–~~	~~–~~
D	6	–	②	–	5	9	–
E	–	9	8	5	–	10	6
F	–	–	–	9	10	–	3
G	–	–	–	–	6	3	–

Now label C with number 2 as it is the second vertex to join the solution and cross out row C. Look for the smallest entry in either column A or column C which is 2 at CD.

Label D with number 3 and cross out row D. Look for the smallest entry in columns A, C and D which is 4 at CB.

1   2 3

	A	B	C	D	E	F	G
~~A~~	~~–~~	~~5~~	~~3~~	~~6~~	~~–~~	~~–~~	~~–~~
B	5	–	④	–	9	–	–
~~C~~	~~③~~	~~4~~	~~–~~	~~2~~	~~8~~	~~–~~	~~–~~
~~D~~	~~6~~	~~–~~	~~②~~	~~–~~	~~5~~	~~9~~	~~–~~
E	–	9	8	5	–	10	6
F	–	–	–	9	10	–	3
G	–	–	–	–	6	3	–

1 4 2 3

	A	B	C	D	E	F	G
~~A~~	~~–~~	~~5~~	~~3~~	~~6~~	~~–~~	~~–~~	~~–~~
~~B~~	~~5~~	~~–~~	~~④~~	~~–~~	~~9~~	~~–~~	~~–~~
~~C~~	~~③~~	~~4~~	~~–~~	~~2~~	~~8~~	~~–~~	~~–~~
~~D~~	~~6~~	~~–~~	~~②~~	~~–~~	~~5~~	~~9~~	~~–~~
E	–	9	8	⑤	–	10	6
F	–	–	–	9	10	–	3
G	–	–	–	–	6	3	–

Label B with number 4 and cross out row B. Look for the smallest entry in columns A, C, D and B which is 5 at DE.

Label E number 5 and cross out row E. Look for the smallest entry in columns A, C, D, B and E which is 6 at EG.

1 4 2 3 5

	A	B	C	D	E	F	G
~~A~~	~~–~~	~~5~~	~~3~~	~~6~~	~~–~~	~~–~~	~~–~~
~~B~~	~~5~~	~~–~~	~~④~~	~~–~~	~~9~~	~~–~~	~~–~~
~~C~~	~~③~~	~~4~~	~~–~~	~~2~~	~~8~~	~~–~~	~~–~~
~~D~~	~~6~~	~~–~~	~~②~~	~~–~~	~~5~~	~~9~~	~~–~~
~~E~~	~~–~~	~~9~~	~~8~~	~~⑤~~	~~–~~	~~10~~	~~6~~
F	–	–	–	9	10	–	3
G	–	–	–	–	⑥	3	–

1 4 2 3 5   6

	A	B	C	D	E	F	G
~~A~~	~~–~~	~~5~~	~~3~~	~~6~~	~~–~~	~~–~~	~~–~~
~~B~~	~~5~~	~~–~~	~~④~~	~~–~~	~~9~~	~~–~~	~~–~~
~~C~~	~~③~~	~~4~~	~~–~~	~~2~~	~~8~~	~~–~~	~~–~~
~~D~~	~~6~~	~~–~~	~~②~~	~~–~~	~~5~~	~~9~~	~~–~~
~~E~~	~~–~~	~~9~~	~~8~~	~~⑤~~	~~–~~	~~10~~	~~6~~
F	–	–	–	9	10	–	③
~~G~~	~~–~~	~~–~~	~~–~~	~~–~~	~~⑥~~	~~3~~	~~–~~

Label G number 6 and cross out row G. Look for the smallest entry in columns A, C, D, B, E and G which is 3 at GF.

Finally label F number 7 and cross out row F. All the vertices are labelled and the spanning tree is complete.

	1	4	2	3	5	7	6
	A	B	C	D	E	F	G
A	–	5	3	6	–	–	–
B	5	–	(4)	–	9	–	–
C	(3)	4	–	2	8	–	–
D	6	–	(2)	–	5	9	–
E	–	9	8	(5)	–	10	6
F	–	–	–	9	10	–	(3)
G	–	–	–	–	(6)	3	–

In the exam you will **not** draw lots of tables like this. You will show all your working on one table, so this last table is how your solution will look.

A ADVICE

The numbers at the top of the columns show the order in which the vertices, and hence the edges, were connected into the solution. The circled numbers give the weights of the edges in the solution so you add these to get the weight of the minimum spanning tree.

Minimum spanning tree

Weight of minimum spanning tree
$3 + 4 + 2 + 5 + 6 + 3 = 23$

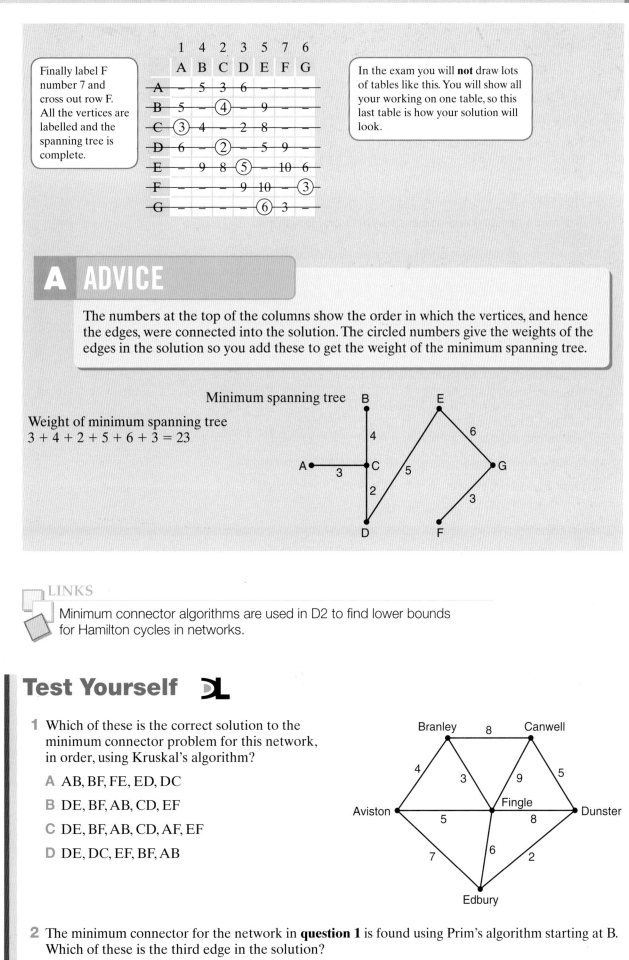

LINKS

Minimum connector algorithms are used in D2 to find lower bounds for Hamilton cycles in networks.

Test Yourself

1 Which of these is the correct solution to the minimum connector problem for this network, in order, using Kruskal's algorithm?

A AB, BF, FE, ED, DC

B DE, BF, AB, CD, EF

C DE, BF, AB, CD, AF, EF

D DE, DC, EF, BF, AB

2 The minimum connector for the network in **question 1** is found using Prim's algorithm starting at B. Which of these is the third edge in the solution?

A AE   B AF   C FE   D DE

3 Jen finds the minimum spanning tree for this network. Which one of the following statements is true for the minimum spanning tree for this network?

A The minimum spanning tree has five edges and length 72.

B The minimum spanning tree has five edges and length 67.

C The minimum spanning tree has six edges and length 90.

D The minimum spanning tree has six edges and length 86.

4 The table shows the distances in kilometres between six towns.
Prim's algorithm starting at F is used on the table to find a minimum connector for the network. Which of the following statements are correct?

1 The minimum connector has weight 19.
2 The minimum connector has weight 18.
3 The edges in the minimum connector are AC, AD, BC, BE, EF.
4 The edges in the minimum connector are AC, AD, BC, DF, EF.
5 The edges in the minimum connector are AC, BC, BE, DF, EF.
6 The fourth edge to join the tree is AC.

	A	B	C	D	E	F
A	–	7	3	4	–	–
B	7	–	4	–	5	6
C	3	4	–	5	9	–
D	4	–	5	–	–	4
E	–	5	9	–	–	3
F	–	6	–	4	3	–

A 1, 3 and 6 are correct

B Only 1 and 5 are correct

C Only 2 and 4 are correct

D 2, 4 and 6 are correct

Exam-Style Question ▷L

The table specifies a road network connecting 6 towns, A to F. The entries give the distances in miles between towns which are connected directly by roads.

	A	B	C	D	E	F
A	–	7	3	–	8	1
B	7	–	4	2	–	7
C	3	4	–	5	9	–
D	–	2	5	–	6	3
E	8	–	9	6	–	–
F	1	7	–	3	–	–

i)   Draw the network.
ii) Use Kruskal's algorithm to find the minimum connector for the network. State clearly the order in which the edges are selected. Draw the resulting tree and give its total length.
iii) Apply the tabular form of Prim's algorithm to the network, starting at vertex A. Show the order in which you connect the vertices. Draw the resulting tree and give its total length.
iii) Comment on the results in parts ii) and iii).

Finding a shortest path

A ABOUT THIS TOPIC

This topic is about finding the shortest path between vertices in a network. The weights on the network could represent many things such as distances, costs of moving objects or time taken to move things. The algorithm enables you to find the shortest route from the starting point to any vertex in the network.

R REMEMBER

- The language and ideas introduced in the Graphs chapter.
- Knowledge of how algorithms can be applied to networks.

K KEY FACTS

- A path is a route from one vertex to another which does not repeat any vertex.

- *Dijkstra's algorithm* is used to find the shortest path between two vertices in a network. The algorithm can be written as a series of steps like this.
  1 Label the start vertex with permanent label 0 and order label 1
  2 Assign temporary labels to all the vertices that can be reached directly from the start vertex. Each temporary label will be the distance from the start vertex.
  3 Select the vertex with the smallest temporary label and make its label permanent. Add the correct order label.
  4 Put temporary labels on each vertex that can be reached directly from the vertex you have just made permanent. The temporary label must be equal to the sum of the new permanent label and the direct distance from it. If there is an existing temporary label at a vertex, it should be replaced only if the new sum is smaller.
  5 Select the vertex with the smallest temporary label and make its label permanent. Add the correct order label.
  6 Repeat until the finishing vertex has a permanent label.
  7 To find the shortest paths(s), trace back from the end vertex to the start vertex. Write the route forwards and state the length.

- When all the vertices have permanent labels, the permanent labels give the shortest distance from the starting vertex to **all** of the other vertices.

EXAMPLE 1

The network shows direct distances in miles between seven villages. Use Dijkstra's algorithm to find the shortest route from A to G.

Reminder: the network is a representation of the real situation. It does not show the exact positions of the vertices and shorter distances can look longer.

A ADVICE

In the exam, the network is usually drawn in the answer booklet with boxes like this to help you show all the working.

Each permanent label shows the distance from the start vertex.

Where you replace working values with smaller numbers, you should show this but do not cross out the original value as the examiner needs to see this working.

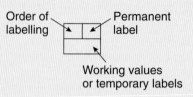

SOLUTION

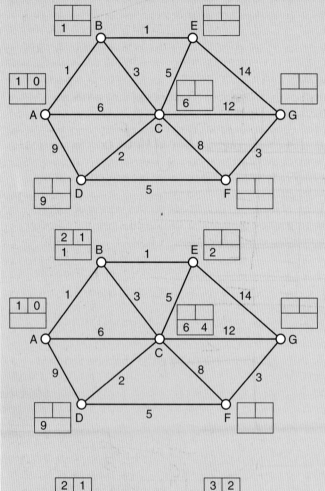

First label the start vertex with a permanent label 0 and order label 1. Put temporary labels on all the vertices that can be reached directly from the start vertex, that is, 1 at B, 6 at C and 9 at D. These labels are the distances from the start vertex.

Select the vertex with the smallest temporary label and make its label permanent. This is vertex B. Put 2 in the box that shows the order of labelling as this is the second vertex to be given a permanent label.
Put temporary labels, equal to the sum of the permanent label and the direct distance from B on each vertex that can be reached directly from B (C and E).
E is given a temporary label $1 + 1 = 2$.
C already has a temporary label 6 but $1 + 3 = 4$ so replace the 6 with 4.
A already has a permanent label.

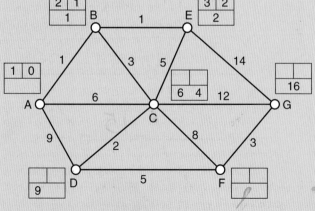

Select the vertex with the smallest temporary label and make its label permanent. This is vertex E. Put 3 in the box that shows the order of labelling as this is the third vertex to be given a permanent label.
Now update the temporary labels on the vertices that can be directly reached from E (G and C).
G is labelled 16 [$2 + 14 = 16$].
C already has a temporary label 4.
$2 + 5 = 7$ which is bigger than 5 so do not replace the temporary label.

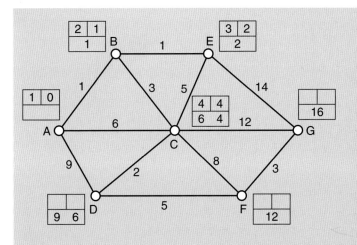

Select the vertex with the smallest temporary label and make its label permanent. This is vertex C. Put 4 in the box that shows the order of labelling as this is the fourth vertex to be given a permanent label.

Now update the temporary labels on the vertices that can be directly reached from C (D, F and G).

The temporary label 9 at D is replaced with 6.

F is given a temporary label 12, G already has a temporary label 16 so don't replace it.

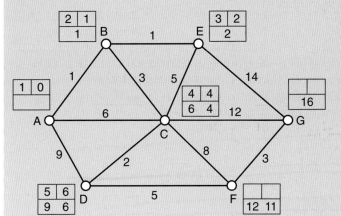

The vertex with the smallest temporary label is vertex D so make this permanent. Put 5 in the box that shows order of labelling as this is the fifth vertex to be given a permanent label.

The only vertex that can be reached directly from D is F.

6 + 5 = 11 which is smaller than 12 so replace the 12 with a temporary label 11.

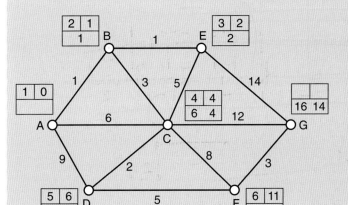

The vertex with the smallest temporary label is vertex F so give F the permanent label 11 and order of labelling 6 as this is the sixth vertex to be given a permanent label.

The only vertex that can be reached directly from F is G.

11 + 3 = 14 which is smaller than 16 so replace the 16 with a temporary label 14.

The only vertex still to be given a label is G so the final step is to label G 14 and order of labelling 7.

The shortest distance from A to G is the permanent label at G so it can be read straight from the network. It is the permanent label at G, 14.

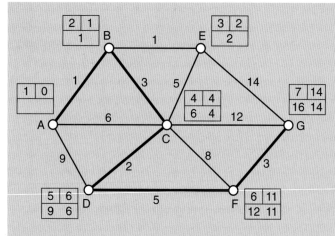

To find the route, trace back through the network, using permanent labels and distances.

The 14 at G came from F since $14 - 3 = 11$.
The 11 at F came from D, $11 - 5 = 6$.
The 6 at D came from C, $6 - 2 = 4$.
The 4 at C came from B, $4 - 3 = 1$.
The 1 at B came from A.

The shortest route from A to G is A B C D F G with length 14 miles.

It is absolutely essential that you show all the working when doing a shortest path question. The examiner is looking for evidence that you have used Dijkstra's algorithm. This evidence is the order of labelling the vertices and the correct working values, especially showing where working values have been replaced when a shorter route is found. Do not cross out temporary labels, write the next temporary label after the old one.

Once the algorithm has been completed, the permanent labels give the shortest distance from the starting vertex to **all** of the vertices.

EXAMPLE 2

What is the shortest distance from A to E? State the route.

SOLUTION

The shortest distance from A to E is 2.
The route is A B E.

> The distance can be read straight from the network. The permanent label at E is 2 so this is the shortest distance.
> The route is found by tracing back.

LINKS

The ideas learnt in this section are extended in D2, where another algorithm, Floyd's algorithm, for finding shortest paths is also studied.

Test Yourself

Use Dijkstra's algorithm to find the shortest path from A to G in this network then answer **questions 1 and 2**.

1 Which of the following statements are true?

1 The shortest paths are ACEG and ADEG.
2 The shortest path is ACDEG.
3 Vertex D has permanent label 6.
4 The sixth vertex to be labelled is F.

A 1 and 3   B 1 and 4   C 3 and 4   D 2 and 4

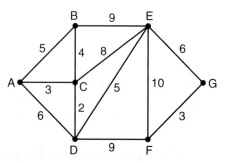

2 Which is the correct labelling at vertex E?

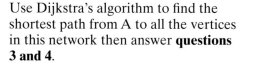

A
5	10
11, 10	

B
5	11
11	

C
5	10
10	

D
5	10
11, 14, 10	

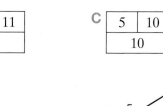

Use Dijkstra's algorithm to find the shortest path from A to all the vertices in this network then answer **questions 3 and 4**.

3 Which is the shortest path from A to F?

  A The only shortest path from A to F is ACF.

  B The only shortest path from A to F is ABEGF.

  C There is more than one shortest path from A to F.

  D The shortest path from A to F is AF.

4 Which of the following statements are correct?

  1 The shortest distance from A to E is 16.
  2 The shortest distance from A to G is 25.
  3 The shortest distance from F to A is 26.
  4 The shortest distance from A to F is 27.

  A 3 only   B 1 and 3   C 2 and 3   D 1, 2 and 4

Exam-Style Question ▶L

The network shows major roads linking nine towns. The number on each edge represents the length, in kilometres, of the road. Alice wishes to drive from her home at A to I. She wants to minimise the distance she travels.

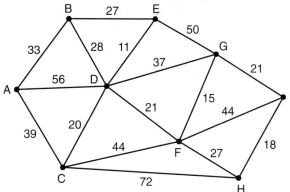

i) Use Dijkstra's algorithm to find the shortest path from A to I. Show all necessary working.
   State the shortest path and its length.
ii) Alice decides to visit her friend who lives at H on the way. Find a path of minimal length that goes from A to I via H and state its length.

A ABOUT THIS TOPIC

This topic is about project planning. A project can be divided into a number of activities that are drawn on a network. This network is then used to identify the activities that must be done on schedule to prevent delaying the whole project.

R REMEMBER

- The language associated with networks.

K KEY FACTS

- *An activity* is a task which needs to be done and takes a given amount of time/resources to complete.

- *Precedence tables* show the activities that need to be done, together with their duration and their immediate predecessors.

- *Precedence networks* show the sequence of the activities. The precedence network must have one start node and one end node.

- *Activities* are represented by *arcs* in the network.

- *Nodes* represent an event which is the start/finish of one or more activities.

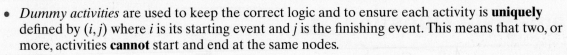

- *Dummy activities* are used to keep the correct logic and to ensure each activity is **uniquely** defined by (i, j) where i is its starting event and j is the finishing event. This means that two, or more, activities **cannot** start and end at the same nodes.

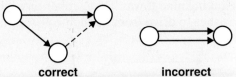

correct   incorrect

- *Forward pass* works out the earliest times that events can happen.

- *Backward pass* works out the latest time that an event can happen.

- *Critical activities* are those which cannot be delayed if the project is to be completed in the minimum time. The critical activities will form a path through the network.

- *Float* is the amount of time by which an activity can be delayed or extended. There are two types of float:
  - *independent float* does not affect other activities
  - *interfering float* is shared between two or more activities.

- There is no float on critical activities.

Drawing a precedence network

In critical path analysis, the first step is to list the activities that need to be done to complete a task, along with the time it takes to complete each one (their duration) and the order in which they need to be done (the precedence). Most questions give a precedence table showing this information and you are asked to draw a precedence network to show this.

 There are two types of precedence network that you might see. The syllabus states that you must use an *activity on arc network* so make sure that this is what you do.

A ADVICE

It can be a good idea to do an initial sketch as it's often possible to make your diagram clearer by repositioning activities to avoid them crossing over one another.

EXAMPLE 1

A project involves eight activities. The durations and precedences are shown in this table.

Draw an activity network for the project.

Activity	Duration (hours)	Immediate predecessors
A	3	–
B	5	–
C	5	A
D	4	A
E	6	A, B
F	2	C, D
G	3	C
H	2	E, F

SOLUTION

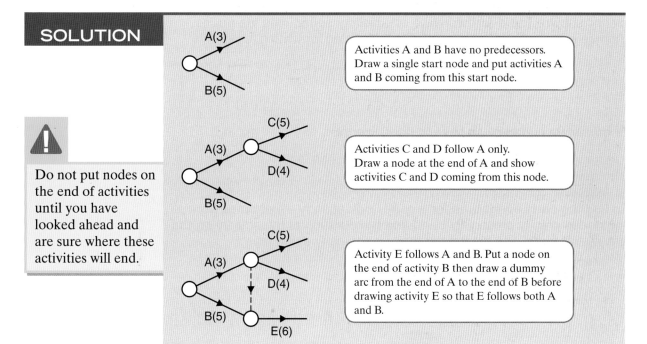

Activities A and B have no predecessors. Draw a single start node and put activities A and B coming from this start node.

Do not put nodes on the end of activities until you have looked ahead and are sure where these activities will end.

Activities C and D follow A only. Draw a node at the end of A and show activities C and D coming from this node.

Activity E follows A and B. Put a node on the end of activity B then draw a dummy arc from the end of A to the end of B before drawing activity E so that E follows both A and B.

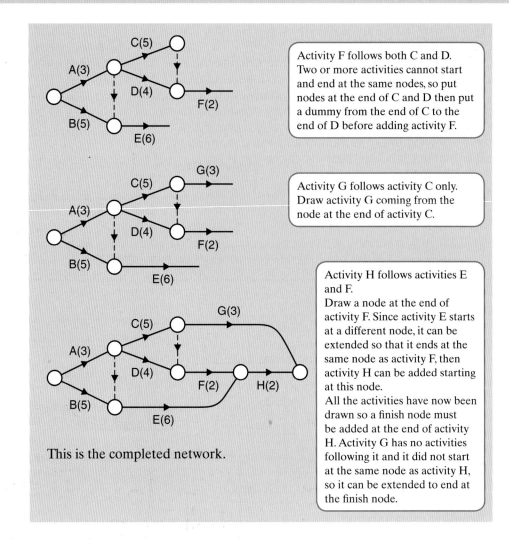

Activity F follows both C and D. Two or more activities cannot start and end at the same nodes, so put nodes at the end of C and D then put a dummy from the end of C to the end of D before adding activity F.

Activity G follows activity C only. Draw activity G coming from the node at the end of activity C.

Activity H follows activities E and F.
Draw a node at the end of activity F. Since activity E starts at a different node, it can be extended so that it ends at the same node as activity F, then activity H can be added starting at this node.
All the activities have now been drawn so a finish node must be added at the end of activity H. Activity G has no activities following it and it did not start at the same node as activity H, so it can be extended to end at the finish node.

This is the completed network.

Forward and backward passes

When doing the forward and backward passes, all the labels must be clearly shown. There are two ways of labelling; sometimes the nodes themselves are drawn with larger divided circles for writing in like this:

early event time   late event time

or boxes are added close to each node like this:

early event time   late event time

To find the **early event time** for a node, look at early event times from all the nodes directly preceding it and add the duration of the activity on the arc joining them. The greatest of these is the early event time.

On the forward pass never put a label on a node till you have labelled the nodes at the start of every arc coming into that node. Once you have done this, work out all the possible values and choose the greatest.

EXAMPLE 2 Perform a forward pass and backward pass on the network. State the minimum completion time for the project and identify the critical activities.

SOLUTION

First perform the forward pass.

Label the start node with an early event time zero.
Activity A has duration 3, add label 3 at the end of A.
E cannot start until both A and B are complete. Activity B has duration 5, so E cannot start until 5 so the early event time is 5.

Now label the node at the end of C since nothing else goes into that node.
3 + 5 = 8, so the early event time is 8.
Two arcs go into the node at the end of D. One is the arc that represents activity D, the time along this route is 3 + 4 = 7. The other is the dummy arc from the end of C, the time along this is 8.
The greater of these values is 8 so add label 8.

The next node to consider is at the end of activities E and F.
The options are along E giving 5 + 6 = 11 or along F giving 8 + 2 = 10.
The greater of these is 11 so the early event time is 11.

Finally consider the finish node. This is at the end of activities G and H.
Along G gives 8 + 3 = 11 or along H gives 11 + 2 = 13.
The greater of these is 13 so the early event time is 13.

Now perform the backward pass.

To find the **late event time** for a node, look at the late event times from all the nodes directly following it and subtract the duration of the activity on the arc joining them. The smallest of these is the **late event time**.

 On the backward pass never put a label on a node till you have labelled the nodes at the end of every arc coming into that node. Once you have done this, work out all the possible values and chose the smallest.

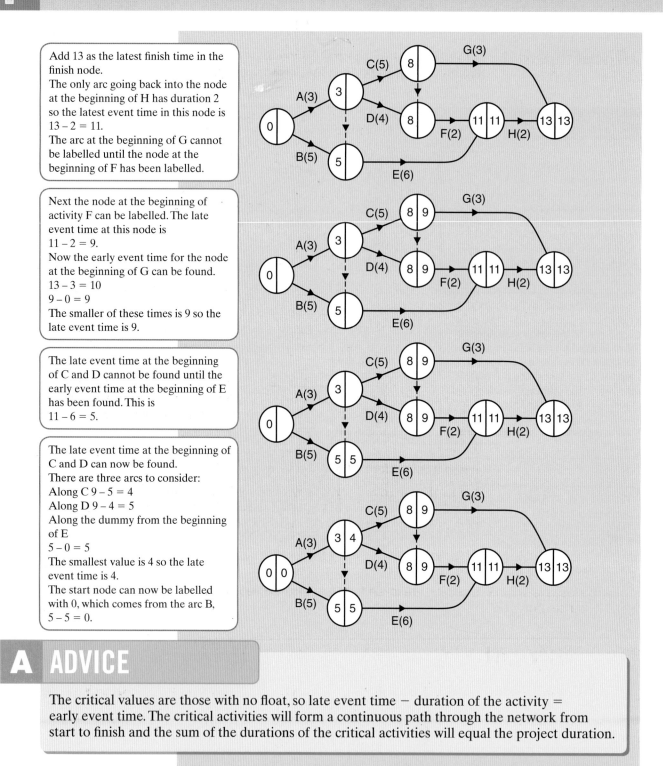

Add 13 as the latest finish time in the finish node.
The only arc going back into the node at the beginning of H has duration 2 so the latest event time in this node is 13 – 2 = 11.
The arc at the beginning of G cannot be labelled until the node at the beginning of F has been labelled.

Next the node at the beginning of activity F can be labelled. The late event time at this node is 11 – 2 = 9.
Now the early event time for the node at the beginning of G can be found.
13 – 3 = 10
9 – 0 = 9
The smaller of these times is 9 so the late event time is 9.

The late event time at the beginning of C and D cannot be found until the early event time at the beginning of E has been found. This is 11 – 6 = 5.

The late event time at the beginning of C and D can now be found.
There are three arcs to consider:
Along C 9 – 5 = 4
Along D 9 – 4 = 5
Along the dummy from the beginning of E
5 – 0 = 5
The smallest value is 4 so the late event time is 4.
The start node can now be labelled with 0, which comes from the arc B, 5 – 5 = 0.

A ADVICE

The critical values are those with no float, so late event time – duration of the activity = early event time. The critical activities will form a continuous path through the network from start to finish and the sum of the durations of the critical activities will equal the project duration.

The minimum completion time is 13 hours (this is the value at the finish node).

The critical activities are B, E, H.

Floats

Activities that are not critical have some spare time so they can be delayed without altering the minimum completion time. Float is the maximum time by which the start of the activity can be delayed without delaying the whole project. There are two types of float, independent and interfering.

Float can be calculated like this:

Latest finish time – earliest start time – duration of activity

But you must always be careful to look at the network to see if the float is independent or interfering. The total float for any activity is the sum of independent float and the interfering float.

| EXAMPLE 3 | For the network in Example 2, find the float for each non-critical activity and say whether it is independent or interfering. |

| SOLUTION | The non-critical activities are A, C, D, F and G. |

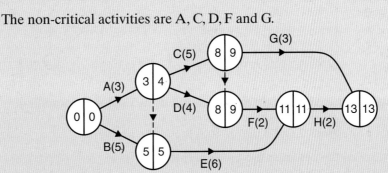

A has duration 3. It can start at 0 but does not have to be finished till 4 so the float on A is $4 - 0 - 3 = 1$ hour.

The float on C is $9 - 3 - 5 = 1$ hour. This is shared with A; if the start of A was delayed by 1 hour, C would not have any float time, so the floats on A and C are interfering floats.

The total float on D is $9 - 3 - 4 = 2$ hours. One hour of this is shared with A; if the start of A was delayed by 1 hour, the float on D would be reduced to 1 hour. The second hour of float is shared with activity F so D has 2 hours of interfering float.

The float on F is $11 - 8 - 2 = 1$ hour but this is shared with A, C and D and so it is interfering float.

The total float on activity G is $13 - 8 - 3 = 2$ hours. One hour of this is shared with A and C so it is interfering float. The second hour of float is not affected by any other activities so this is independent float.

LINKS

The ideas learnt in this section are taken further in the next section on resource allocation.

Test Yourself

1 Which is the correct network for the table?

Activity	Immediate predecessors
A	–
B	–
C	–
D	A, B
E	B, C
F	D, E
G	D

A

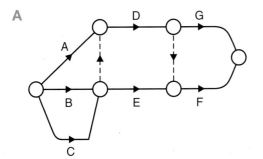

B

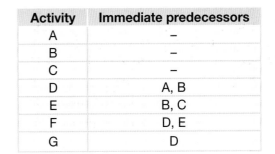

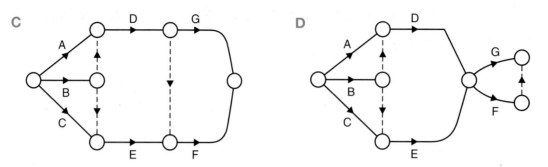

Make sure you have the right answer to **question 1** before proceeding.

Now answer **questions 2 and 3** before looking at the answers.

The durations of the activities are given in this table.
Perform a forward and backward pass on the network.

Activity	Immediate predecessors	Duration (hours)
A	–	2
B	–	3
C	–	4
D	A, B	4
E	B, C	2
F	D, E	2
G	D	3

2 Which are the correct early and late times for the event at the end of activity E?

　　A 6, 7　　　　　　　**B** 7, 7　　　　　　　**C** 6, 8　　　　　　**D** 7, 8

3 Which of these gives the critical activities and the duration of the project?

　　A B, D, G duration 10 hours

　　B C, E, F duration 8 hours

　　C A, D, G duration 9 hours

　　D A, B, D, G duration 10 hours

4 Draw the activity network for the project in this precedence table. Perform a forward and backward pass then select the correct answer from these choices.

Activity	Immediate predecessors	Duration (hours)
A	–	2
B	–	0.5
C	A	1.5
D	A, B	2
E	A, B	5
F	E	6
G	C, D	10
H	F, G	1

　A There are no activities with independent float.

　B All the floats are independent floats.

　C Activities B and C have independent float; E and F have interfering float.

　D Activities B, E and F share interfering float.

Exam-Style Question ⊃L

The table shows activities involved in making a salad, their precedences and their durations.

	Activity	Immediate predecessor(s)	Duration (minutes)
A	Wash the salad ingredients	–	3
B	Slice tomato	A	2
C	Slice cucumber	A	1.5
D	Chop lettuce	A	1.5
E	Peel onion	–	1
F	Slice onion	E	2
G	Prepare herbs	–	1.5
H	Mix the salad dressing	–	3
I	Collect ingredients in bowl	B, C, D, F, G	1
J	Add dressing	H, I	1

i) Draw an activity network for preparing the salad.
ii) Perform a forward pass and a backward pass to determine early and late event times. Give the critical activities and the minimum time needed to make the salad.

Resource allocation

A ABOUT THIS TOPIC

This topic continues the work done in the previous section and looks at how the information gained from drawing a network and identifying the critical activities can be used to allocate workers to a project in the most efficient way.

R REMEMBER

- The work covered in the previous section 'Precedence tables and activity networks'.

K KEY FACTS

- **Float** is the amount of time by which an activity can be delayed or extended.

- Float = latest finish time − earliest start time − duration of activity.

- There are two types of float:
  - independent float does not affect other activities
  - interfering float is shared between two or more activities.

- *Cascade chart* shows the order of activities in a project against a time scale. It is sometimes called a *Gantt chart*.

- *Resource histogram* shows the quantity of resources (usually number of people) needed to do the activities at any given time in a project.

- *Resource levelling* – when planning a project, it may be desirable to minimise the resources at any given time or to complete the project as quickly or as cheaply as possible. Resource levelling looks at ways in which you can do this.

Drawing a cascade chart

In the previous section, Example 1 produced this activity network:

You can represent this information on a cascade chart.

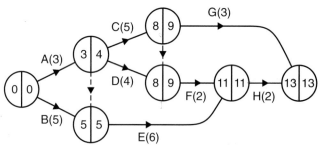

Activity	Duration (hours)	Immediate predecessors
A	3	–
B	5	–
C	5	A
D	4	A
E	6	A, B
F	2	C, D
G	3	C
H	2	E, F

EXAMPLE 1

Show the information for the project above on a cascade chart, given that all the activities are scheduled to start as early as possible.

SOLUTION

Start by drawing a table with the activities down the left-hand side and the time scale along the top.

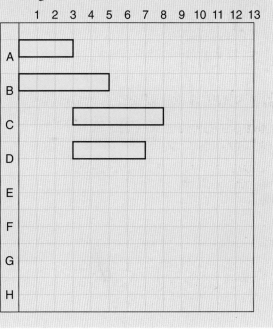

It is easier to draw the cascade chart by looking at the network.

Activities A and B can start at the beginning, so draw bars to show them starting at 0 and ending at 3 and 5 respectively.

C and D follow A so they can both start at time 3. Draw the bars showing their durations starting at time 3.

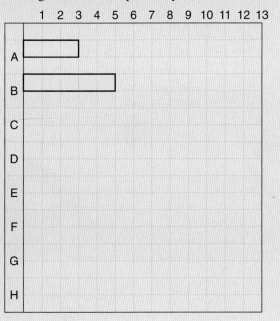

E follows A and B so it cannot start until B is finished at 5. It has duration 6 so will end at time 11.

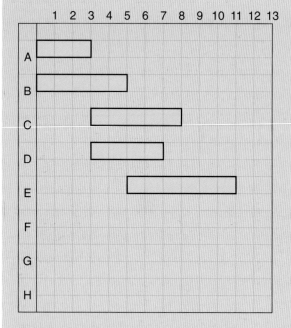

F follows C and D and has duration 2 so it can start at time 8 and will finish at 10.

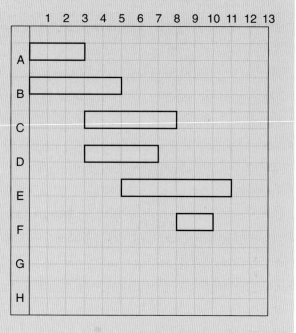

G follows C and has duration 3 so it starts at 8 and ends at 11.

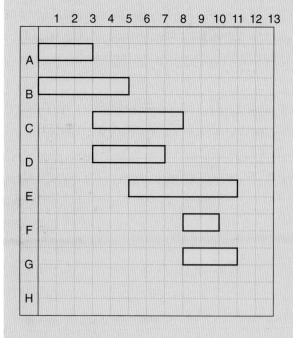

H has duration 2 and follows E and F so it starts at 11 and ends at 13.

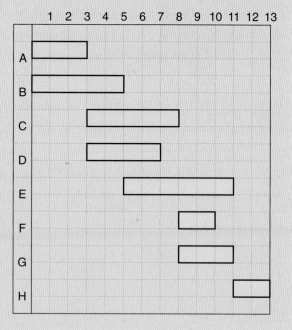

Showing useful information on your cascade chart

Critical activities

The critical activities are B, E, H (see Example 2 of the previous section). These can be shaded to make it clear which activities are critical.

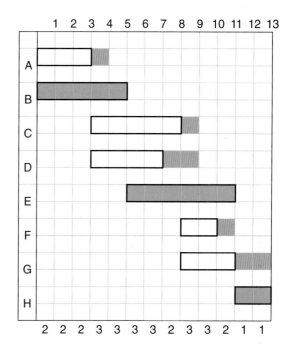

A ADVICE

When you are doing this in the exam you will almost always have drawn the network and found the critical activities earlier in the question. Don't forget to use this information.

Floats

Floats on activities can also be shown on the cascade chart by shading in a different style or colour outside the bar:

A does not have to be finished till 4 so the float on A is 1 hour.

C does not have to finish till 9 so the float on C is also1 hour.

The float on D is 2 hours.

The float on F is 1 hour

The float on G is 2 hours.

(See Example 3 of the previous section.)

Once you have drawn a cascade chart, you can use it to draw a resource histogram that shows the number of people needed at any time in the project.

A ADVICE

It can be useful to put the total number needed for each hour at the bottom of the chart to help you draw the resource histogram. This has been done on the cascade chart above.

EXAMPLE 2   Draw a resource histogram for the project in Example 1, assuming each activity starts at the earliest possible time.

SOLUTION

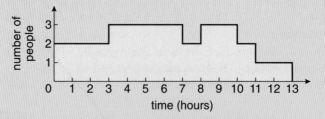

For the first 3 hours, A and B are going on so two people are needed.

Between 3 and 5 hours, B, C and D are going on and between 5 and 7 hours, C, D and E are going on. So three people are needed from 3 hours to 7 hours.

From 7 until 8 hours, C and E are going on so two people are needed.
From 8 until 10 E, F and G are being done so three people are needed.
From 10 until 11 E and G are still being done so two people are needed.
From 11 until 13 hours, only H is going on, so only one person is needed.

A ADVICE

Sometimes more than one person is needed for each task. In this case the number of people can be written on the cascade chart above the bars and this can then be shown on the resource histogram.

EXAMPLE 3

In Example 1, the project planner realises that they have not taken account of the number of people needed for each task. The correct information is shown in this table.

Draw a new resource histogram.

How many workers are now needed to complete the project?

Activity	Duration (hours)	Immediate predecessors	Number of people
A	3	–	2
B	5	–	2
C	5	A	3
D	4	A	2
E	6	A, B	1
F	2	C, D	3
G	3	C	1
H	2	E, F	2

SOLUTION

Putting the numbers of workers onto the cascade chart gives this diagram.

Remember: it can be useful to put the total needed for each hour at the bottom of the chart to help you draw the resource histogram.

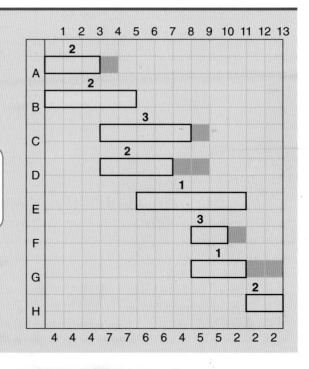

The resource histogram now looks like this.

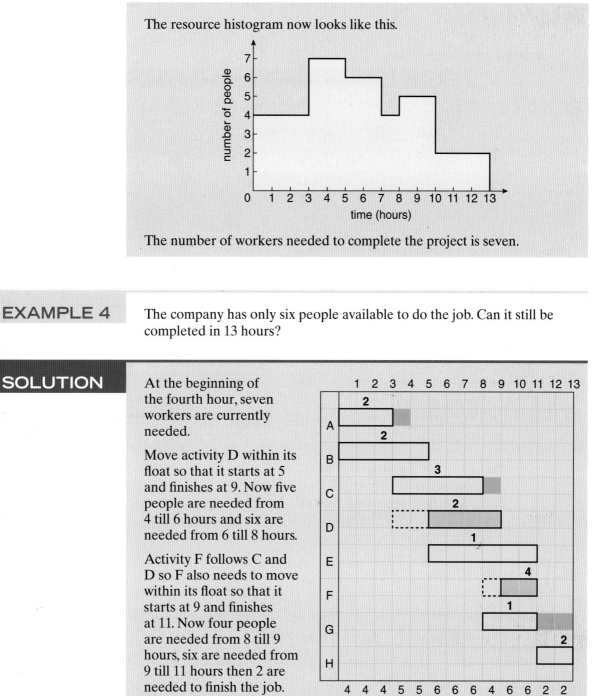

The number of workers needed to complete the project is seven.

EXAMPLE 4

The company has only six people available to do the job. Can it still be completed in 13 hours?

SOLUTION

At the beginning of the fourth hour, seven workers are currently needed.

Move activity D within its float so that it starts at 5 and finishes at 9. Now five people are needed from 4 till 6 hours and six are needed from 6 till 8 hours.

Activity F follows C and D so F also needs to move within its float so that it starts at 9 and finishes at 11. Now four people are needed from 8 till 9 hours, six are needed from 9 till 11 hours then 2 are needed to finish the job.

So the job can be completed in 13 hours with six workers.

LINKS

Critical path analysis is used extensively in Business Studies and any area of work where project planning is important.

Test Yourself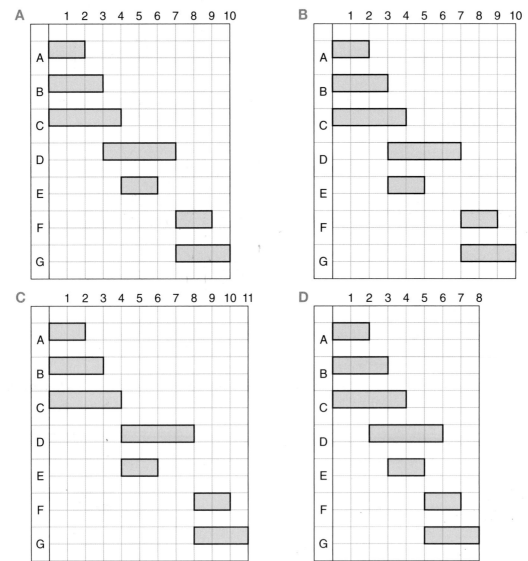

1 Look at this precedence table.

Activity	Immediate predecessors	Duration (hours)
A	–	2
B	–	3
C	–	4
D	A, B	4
E	B, C	2
F	D, E	2
G	D	3

Which is the correct cascade chart for the table?

Questions 2 and 3 refer to this network and cascade chart.

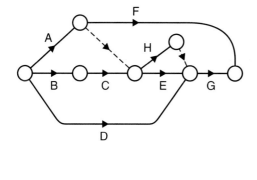

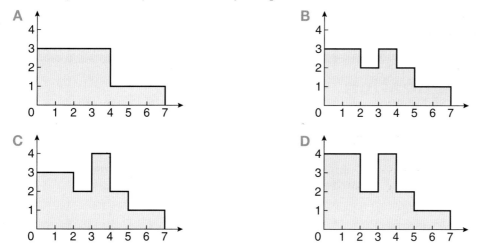

2 Assuming each activity can be done by one person, choose the correct resource histogram.

3 It is decided that activity A cannot be started until activity B is completed. Look at the following statements; choose the ones that are true.

       P The project can be completed in the same time.

       Q The project will take 8 hours to complete.

       R The number of people needed to complete the project in the minimum time is three.

       S It needs the same number of people to complete it.

A Q and R   **B** P and S   **C** Q and S   **D** P and R

4 The table shows the precedences for a project. The floats on activities A, C, D and G are shaded on the cascade chart.

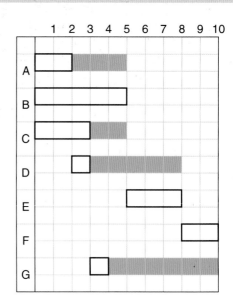

Activity	Immediate predecessors
A	–
B	–
C	–
D	A
E	A, B, C
F	D, E
G	C

Find the minimum number of people needed to complete the project in 10 days and state which activities need to be moved within their float.

A 3 people, no activities need to be moved

B 3 people, move activities C and G

C 2 people, move activities A and D

D 2 people, move activities A, D and G

Exam-Style Question ▷L

The table shows activities involved in decorating a room, their precedences, durations and the number of workers needed at any one time to complete each activity.

	Activity	Immediate predecessor(s)	Duration (hours)	Number of workers
A	Remove fittings	–	1	3
B	Strip the wallpaper	A	2	1
C	Remove old paint	A	3	1
D	Replaster the walls	B, C	3	2
E	Sand the woodwork	B, C	2	1
F	Paint the ceiling	E	6	1
G	Paint the woodwork	E	4	2
H	Paint the walls	D	4	2
I	Clean up	F, G, H	2	3
J	Replace fittings	I	1	3

i) Draw a cascade chart, assuming each activity starts at the earliest possible time.

ii) State the duration of the project and identify the critical activities.

iii) Draw a resource histogram for the project and state the maximum number of workers needed at any one time.

iv) There are only 4 workers available for the project. The manager believes he can complete the project in a slightly longer time with 4 workers by reducing the number of workers from 2 to 1 on one activity, but this will double the time it takes. Which activity should he choose and what is the new completion time? What effect does this have on the critical activities?

Linear programming

Formulation and graphical solution

▶▶ 139
148

A ABOUT THIS TOPIC

This topic is about optimisation, for example, making the maximum profit or using the minimum resources.

R REMEMBER

- How to draw a straight line graph from an equation from GCSE and C1.
- How to shade a region on a graph to represent an inequality from GCSE.
- How to manipulate inequalities from C1.

K KEY FACTS

The graphical method is for solving linear programming problems in two unknowns.

Graphical method for solving problems with two variables

1 Define the variables.
2 Define the constraints.
3 Define the objective function (the function which is to be maximised or minimised).
4 Graph the feasible region.
5 Find the co-ordinates of the corner points.
6 Substitute the co-ordinates of the corner points into the objective function to see which gives the optimal value.

Linear programming problems

Linear programming deals with problems such as maximising profits, minimising costs or ensuring you make the best use of available resources. Linear programming is an optimisation tool, which allows the best decision given certain restrictions.

Formulating a linear program (LP) problem

1 Define the variables

The problems in D1 are designed to be solved using a graph so they will have two variables, one on the x axis and one on the y axis. Every linear programming problem starts with identifying and defining the variables about which a decision is to be made (these are sometimes called the decision variables).

5

EXAMPLE 1

Alan is making cakes to raise money for charity. He wants to make chocolate cakes and plain cakes. Each chocolate cake needs 4 eggs, 100 g of butter and 300 g of flour. Each plain cake needs 2 eggs, 200 g of butter and 300 g of flour. Alan has 70 eggs, 3 kg of butter and 6 kg of flour. He has more than enough of the other ingredients he needs. He sells each chocolate cake for £3.50 and each plain cake for £2.50. How many of each type of cake should Alan make in order to maximise the money he raises? Define the variables for Alan's cake problem.

SOLUTION

Let x be the number of chocolate cakes made. Let y be the number of plain cakes made.

⚠ You must be very precise in the way you define the variables. It is not sufficient to say 'let x be chocolate cakes', you must say 'let x be the **number of** chocolate cakes made'.

2 Constraints

Constraints are limits on the values which the decision variables can take. There will be at least two constraints in a two variable problem. Since the number of cakes cannot be negative, $x \geq 0$ and $y \geq 0$. These are called **trivial constraints.**

A ADVICE

It is sometimes helpful to put the information from the question into a table to help you.

Each chocolate cake needs 4 eggs, 100 g of butter and 300 g of flour. Each plain cake needs 2 eggs, 200 g of butter and 300 g of flour. Alan has 70 eggs, 3 kg of butter and 6 kg of flour.

	Eggs	Butter	Flour
Chocolate cake (x)	4	100	300
Plain cake (y)	2	200	300
Total available	70	3000	6000

Note that these have been changed to grams.

EXAMPLE 2

Show that one of the constraints leads to the inequality $x + y \leq 20$.

SOLUTION

Notice that there is the same number of each type of cake in this inequality.

Looking at the table you can see that the only ingredient that uses the same amount for both cakes is flour.

The flour constraint is $300x + 300y \leq 6000$.

⚠ Be careful to use the units consistently. In this example some weights are given in grams and some are given in kilograms. You must convert everything into the same units before you write the constraints.

You can simplify this by dividing through by 300 to give $x + y \leq 20$.

EXAMPLE 3 Find the other constraints for this problem.

SOLUTION

There are two other ingredients, so there will be one constraint for each one.

Eggs:

$$4x + 2y \leqslant 70$$

Divide each side by 2

$$2x + y \leqslant 35$$

Butter:

$$100x + 200y \leqslant 3000$$

Divide each side by 100

$$x + 2y \leqslant 30$$

> Notice that the constraints have been simplifed by cancelling.

The objective function

The objective function is a linear function of x and y which is to be optimised; if you are trying to find a profit it must be maximised but if you are calculating cost it will be minimised.

 When you are defining the objective function it is important to state whether you are to maximise or minimise.

EXAMPLE 4 What is the objective function for Alan's cake problem?

SOLUTION **Maximise P = 3.5x + 2.5y**

> Remember that Alan sells each chocolate cake for £3.50 and each plain cake for £2.50.

Graphical solution of a linear programming problem

Once you have formulated the problem, you will be asked to solve it graphically. This means you must draw a graph and the inequalities that represent the constraints, then use the graph to find the best solution.

 When showing the inequalities it is important to shade the unwanted region.

EXAMPLE 5 Show the inequalities on a graph.

SOLUTION

A ADVICE

You need to graph the three inequalities. To work out where to draw the lines and the scales for the axes, it is a good idea to work out where the lines that define the inequalities will cut the x and y axes.

So $x + y = 20$ cuts the axes at $(0, 20)$ and $(20, 0)$.

For $2x + y = 35$, when $x = 0$, $y = 35$ and when $y = 0$, $2x = 35$ so $2x + y = 35$ cuts the axes at $(0, 35)$ and $(17.5, 0)$.

$x + 2y = 30$ cuts the axes at $(0, 15)$ and $(30, 0)$.

Draw the x axis from 0 to 30.
Draw the y axis from 0 to 35.

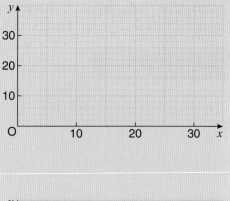

Plot the line $x + y = 20$ and shade the unwanted region to show $x + y \leq 20$ unshaded.

 Remember to shade the unwanted region.

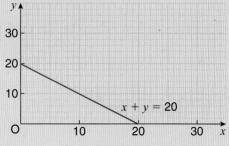

On the line $x + y = 20$, you want $x + y$ to be smaller than (or equal to) 20 so you don't want the bit above the line.

Plot the line $2x + y = 35$ and shade the unwanted region to show $2x + y \leq 35$ unshaded.

$2x + y = 35$ goes through $(0, 35)$ and $(17.5, 0)$.

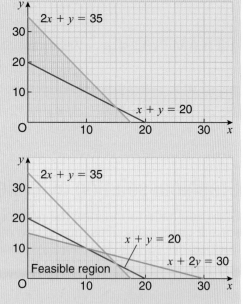

Plot the line $x + 2y = 30$ and shade the unwanted region to show $x + 2y \leq 30$ unshaded.

$x + 2y = 30$ goes through $(0, 15)$ and $(30, 0)$.

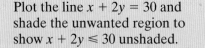

The graph is now complete. The solution must lie in the **unshaded** region. This is called the *feasible region*.

Finding the best solution

The best, or optimal, solution is the one which gives the maximum profit or minimum cost, depending on the type of problem. To find this you must consider the value of the objective function. The best solution is always at a vertex of the feasible region so a tour from vertex to vertex will lead to the optimal solution.

 You must be able to find the solution to problems from the graph. Make sure you can draw graphs accurately.

Method

Find the co-ordinates of all the vertices of the feasible region.
Calculate the value of the objective function at each vertex.

EXAMPLE 6

Use your graph to find out how many of each type of cake Alan should make in order to maximise the money he raises.

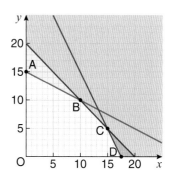

SOLUTION

First identify the vertices of the feasible region.

A $(0, 15)$
B $(10, 10)$
C $(15, 5)$
D $(17.5, 0)$

> **A ADVICE**
>
> This is a maximisation problem; $(0, 0)$ is a vertex in the feasible region. However, the profit at $(0, 0)$ will be zero so there is no need to include this in the working here.

Now calculate the value of the money raised at each vertex by using the objective function, $P = 3.5x + 2.5y$.

To show working, a table can be used

Vertex	x	y	$P = 3.5x + 2.5y$
A	0	15	$0 + 2.5 \times 15 = 37.50$
B	10	10	$3.5 \times 10 + 2.5 \times 10 = 60.00$
C	15	5	$3.5 \times 15 + 2.5 \times 5 = 65.00$

At **A** $x = 0, y = 15$ so P = £37.50
At **B** $x = 10, y = 10$ so P = £60.00
At **C** $x = 15, y = 5$ so P = £65.00
At **D** $x = 17.5, y = 0$ this is not a valid solution because Alan must make a whole number of cakes. So x can't be 17.5.

 It is easy to assume that you should use $x = 17.5, y = 0$, since this is obviously in the feasible region, but if you look closely at the graph near point D you can see that $(17, 1)$ is also in the feasible region and this will be a possible solution. This is dealt with in more detail in the next section.

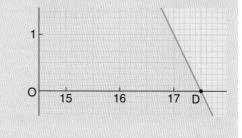

$$x = 17, y = 1$$
$$P = 3.5 \times 17 + 2.5 \times 1 = 62$$
so $P = £62.00$

So the best solution is for Alan to make 15 chocolate cakes and 5 plain cakes. He will make £65.00.

Minimisation problems

Sometimes the problem asks you to minimise the cost rather than maximise the profit.

EXAMPLE 7

The graph shows the feasible region for the following linear programming problem.

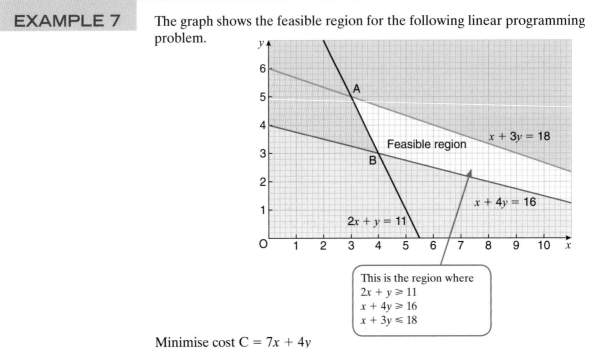

This is the region where
$2x + y \geqslant 11$
$x + 4y \geqslant 16$
$x + 3y \leqslant 18$

Minimise cost $C = 7x + 4y$
subject to: $2x + y \geqslant 11, x + 4y \geqslant 16, x + 3y \leqslant 18$.

Find the optimal solution and state the minimum value of C.

SOLUTION

Calculate the value of C at each vertex of the feasible region.

At **A** $x = 3, y = 5$ so C = 41.
At **B** $x = 4, y = 3$ so C = 40.

The optimal solution is $x = 4, y = 3$, with a cost of £40.00.

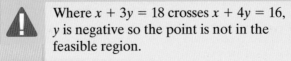

Where $x + 3y = 18$ crosses $x + 4y = 16$, y is negative so the point is not in the feasible region.

LINKS

The ideas learnt in this section are very important in the next section and for D2. Linear programming is widely used in business and industry.

Test Yourself ▶️

The Test Yourself questions all relate to the following problem.
Carrie is making cushions and rag dolls to sell at a local craft fair. A cushion takes 40 minutes to make and the materials cost £10.00. Each doll takes an hour to make and the materials cost £6.00. She has room to display at most six cushions. Carrie has £72 to spend on materials and has nine hours available to make the products.

1 The decision variables for this problem are:

A Let x be cushions and y be dolls.

B Let x be profit and y be cost of materials.

C Let x be number of cushions made and y be number of dolls made.

D Let x be time in minutes and let y be materials.

Make sure you have got question 1 right before going on to question 2.

2 Carrie sells the cushions for £15 each and the dolls for £10 each and she wants to make as much profit as she can. The objective function for this problem is:

A Minimise $P = 10x + 6y$

B $P = 5x + 4y$

C Maximise $P = 15x + 10y$

D Maximise $P = 5x + 4y$

3 The constraints for this problem are:

A $2x + 3y \leqslant 27$
$5x + 3y \leqslant 36$

B $2x + 3y \leqslant 27$
$5x + 3y \leqslant 36$
$x \leqslant 6$

C $40x + y \leqslant 9$
$5x + 3y \leqslant 36$
$x \leqslant 6$

D $2x + 3y \leqslant 27$
$5x + 3y \leqslant 36$
$x \geqslant 6$

Make sure you have got questions 1–3 right before going on to question 4.

4 The solution of the problem is:

A Make 6 cushions and 2 dolls with a profit of £38.

B Make 9 dolls.

C Profit = £43

D Make 3 cushions and 7 dolls with a profit of £43.

Exam-Style Question ▶️

A takeaway makes small and large pizzas. Each day they must make at least 40 of each size and they will sell no more than 400 pizzas in total. They make a profit of £2.00 on each small pizza and £3.00 on each large pizza.

The small pizzas take 2 minutes to make and the large pizzas take 4 minutes to make. There are four workers who are each available for 5 hours a day.

i) Given that x is the number of small pizzas made and y is the number of large pizzas made, show that one of the constraints leads to the inequality $x + 2y \leqslant 600$.

ii) Formulate this situation as a linear programming problem to maximise profit.

iii) Use a graphical method to solve the problem.

Integer programming and spare capacity

K **KEY FACTS**

• Some problems will have more than one optimal solution.

• Some LP problems must have integer solutions.

• The solution to an LP problem may need to be adapted to account for changes in the constraints.

More than one solution

Sometimes LP problems can have more than one optimal solution.

EXAMPLE 1

The graph shows the feasible region for this LP problem:

Maximise $P = x + y$
subject to $y \leq 4x, x + y \leq 10,$
$4x + y \leq 20, x \geq 0, y \geq 0.$

Find the optimal solution to the problem.

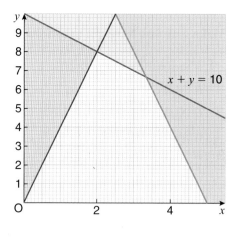

SOLUTION

The natural assumption is that the optimal solution will lie at either **A** or **B**.

However, notice that the objective function $P = x + y$ has the same gradient as $x + y = 10$, the boundary for one of the constraints, $x + y \leq 10$. This means that when $P = 10$, all the points on the line $P = x + y$ will give a profit of 10, which is the maximum for this problem.

So all points on the constraint line $x + y = 10$ will be optimal.

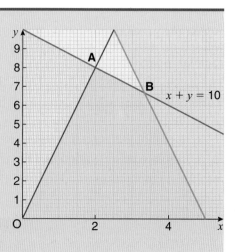

Integer solutions

The solution to an LP problem is not necessarily a whole number.

In reality there are many situations where the solution must take an integer value, for example, when trying to find the number of products a company should produce.

EXAMPLE 2

A company produces two items A and B; x is the number of item A produced and y is the number of item B produced. The profit per item is shown in the table.

Product	Number made	Profit per item
A	x	£50.00
B	y	£10.00

They are subject to constraints

$$30x + 9y \leqslant 3700$$
$$30x + 4y \leqslant 2000$$
$$y \geqslant 75$$
$$x \geqslant 0$$

The graph for this problem is like this:

The company must make a whole number of each product. How many of each product should the company make in order to maximise its profit?

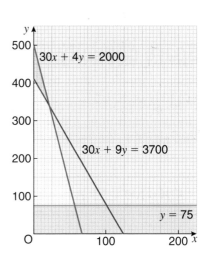

SOLUTION

The profit, £P, is given by $P = 50x + 10y$.

The vertices of the feasible region are:

$(0, 411\frac{1}{9})$ Profit = £4111.11

$(21\frac{1}{3}, 340)$ Profit = £4466.67

$(56\frac{2}{3}, 75)$ Profit = £3583.33

So the best solution appears to be when $x = 21\frac{1}{3}$ $y = 340$ but this is not a valid solution because x is not an integer.

A ADVICE

To find the co-ordinates of the second vertex, you could solve the simultaneous equations $30x + 4y = 2000$, $30x + 9y = 3700$, but in the D1 exam it is only necessary to draw a good graph and read the co-ordinates from the graph. You would not get any extra marks for solving the simultaneous equations.

 When a problem has an integer solution but the 'optimal' vertex does not give integer values, you must check all the integer points in the feasible region near the optimal vertex.

The obvious point to check is $x = 21, y = 340$, giving $P = £4450$.

Looking carefully at the graph near the optimal vertex, you can see that the point $(21, 341)$ is also in the feasible region.

You can check that $(21, 341)$ satisfies
$30x + 9y \leqslant 3700$.

$30 \times 21 + 9 \times 341 = 3699 < 3700$.

$(21, 341)$ gives a profit of £4460 so this is the optimal solution.

Make 21 of product A and 341 of product B.
Profit = £4460.

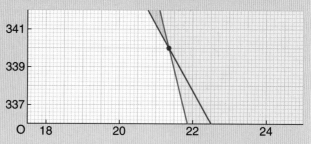

For problems with integer solutions, first find the optimal vertex then look at integer points near it.

Spare capacity

Spare capacity refers to situations where one or more of the resources is not fully used up.

Unused resources are associated with the constraints that do not pass through the optimal vertex.

EXAMPLE 3

Brian's Toys makes two kinds of cars.

Car A sells for a profit of £2.50 and car B sells for a profit (P) of £3.00.

Department	Car A	Car B	Time available
Manufacturing	1.5	3	45
Assembly	2	1	35
Painting	0.25	0.25	5

The time needed in each of the departments, in hours, is shown in this table along with the time available in each department every week.

Which department has spare capacity? State how much time is unused.

SOLUTION

The problem is formulated as: Let x be the number of car A made.
Let y be the number of car B made.

Maximise $P = 2.5x + 3y$.

$1.5x + 3y \leqslant 45$
so $3x + 6y \leqslant 90$ (Subject to manufacturing)
        $x + 2y \leqslant 30$

$2x + y \leqslant 35$ (assembly)

$0.25x + 0.25y \leqslant 5$
so $x + y \leqslant 20$ (painting)

> Notice that the first and third constraints have been scaled up to give integer coefficients.

The graphical solution is shown on the graph.

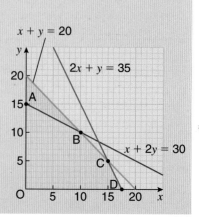

At vertex A $(0, 15)$ P = £45.00
At vertex B $(10, 10)$ P = £55.00
At vertex C $(15, 5)$ P = £52.50
At vertex D $(17.5, 0)$ P = £43.75

So the optimal solution is to make 10 of each car, giving a profit of £55.00.

This occurs at vertex B which is where the constraints for manufacturing and painting cross over, so the constraint that is not all used is the assembly constraint $2x + y \leqslant 35$.

If $x = 10$ and $y = 10$, this uses $20 + 10 = 30$ hours so there are 5 hours of time unused in the assembly department.

Changing a constraint

EXAMPLE 4

Brian decides that he can afford to keep the paint shop open for 6 hours each week. Given that he must produce a whole number of toys, what effect does this have on his profit? Comment on the decision to increase the hours available in the paint shop.

SOLUTION

The decision changes the constraint $x + y \leqslant 20$ to $0.25x + 0.25y \leqslant 6$, i.e. $x + y \leqslant 24$, which is equivalent to a translation of the boundary, 4 units parallel to the y axis.

If you add this new line to the graph you can see that the optimal vertex has changed. It is now where the constraints $2x + y \leqslant 35$ and $3x + 6y \leqslant 90$ intersect at $x = 13\frac{1}{2}, y = 8\frac{1}{3}$.

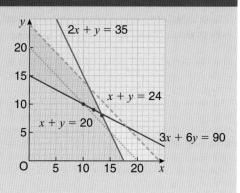

This is a new vertex for the feasible region but this is not a valid solution as these are not integer values.

The red dots show the integer solutions near the optimal vertex.

Looking at the integer points near the intersection of the two constraints gives three possibilities:

$x = 12, y = 9$ P = £57
$x = 14, y = 7$ P = £56
$x = 13, y = 8$ P = £56.50

> Remember
> $P = 2.5x + 3y$.

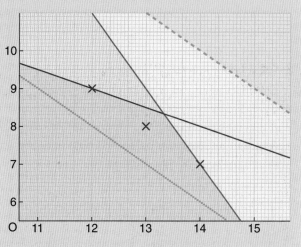

so the best solution now is to make 12 of car A and 9 of car B giving a profit of £57.00.

This is only a £2.00 increase on his previous profit. It can be seen from the graph that the constraint for the paint shop is now completely outside the feasible region, so the increase of 1 hour has had little effect.

The same increase could have been achieved by increasing the time for the paintshop by $\frac{1}{4}$ hour, so that the constraint was $0.25x + 0.25y \leqslant 5\frac{1}{4}$ so $x + y \leqslant 21$.

📚 LINKS

The ideas learnt in this section are very important in D2 for understanding the simplex method for solving linear programming problems with more than two variables.

Test Yourself ▶L

1 The graph shows the optimal vertex for a linear programming problem where the solution must be an integer.

The objective function is to maximise the profit where $P = 6x + 8y$.

What is the maximum profit?

A £74   B £85.40   C £82   D £88

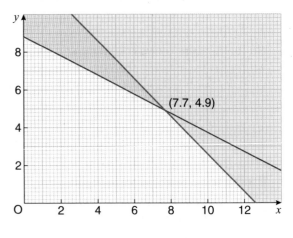

Questions 2, 3 and 4 are about the following problem.
A company makes two types of wooden chair.

Type X requires 2 hours of machine time and 5 hours of craftsman time. It takes 3 hours to paint and earns £40 profit.

Type Y requires 4 hours of machine time and 5 hours of craftsman time. It takes 4 hours to paint and earns £70 profit.

Each day there are 35 hours of machine time and 63 hours of craftsman time available and 40 hours of painting time.

The graphical solution is

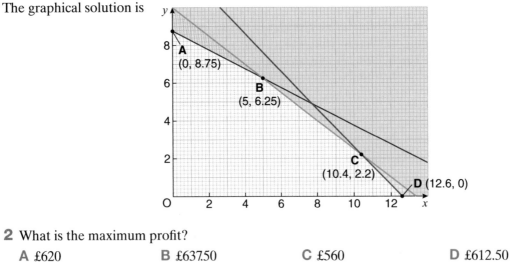

2 What is the maximum profit?

A £620   B £637.50   C £560   D £612.50

3 The manager decides to employ the craftsmen for 65 hours. How does this affect the solution?

A It will increase the profit without changing the optimal vertex.

B It will decrease the profit.

C It will increase the profit and change the optimal vertex.

D It will have no effect on the solution.

4 The company decide to run a special offer and reduce the prices of the chairs so that the profit on type X is £30 and the profit on type Y is £40. What effect does this have on the solution to the problem?

A It has no effect on the number of each type of chair they should make.

B There are now several possible combinations that will make the same profit.

C They should make more of type Y because this makes more profit.

D 8 of type X and 4 of type Y gives the maximum profit.

Exam-Style Question ▷L

A market trader stocks two types of jacket; type A cost him £30 to buy and type B cost him £50 to buy. He has £6000 to spend on jackets. He needs to order at least 120 jackets to satisfy demand over the winter and he believes he will be able to sell at least 50 of the more expensive jackets. Type A jackets each need 20 cm of storage space whereas type B are thicker and need 40 cm of storage space. He has 45 m of storage space for jackets. He sells type A jackets for £50 and type B for £80.

Let x be the number of type A jackets and y be the number of type B jackets.

i)   Explain why the objective function is to maximise $P = 20x + 30y$.

ii)   Explain why one of the constraints is $2x + 4y \leqslant 450$.

iii) Write three further constraints for the problem.

iv)   Assuming that he can sell all the jackets he buys, how many of each type should he stock in order to maximise his profits?

v)   The trader realises that he can afford to spend £6500 on buying jackets. Will this improve the optimal solution? Justify your answer.

Simulation

Monte Carlo methods

A ABOUT THIS TOPIC

This section is about using random devices, especially random number generators, to simulate events which are affected by chance. Simulations allow you to see what might happen. They can be done very quickly on computers.

R REMEMBER

- Basic probability from GCSE.

K KEY FACTS

- Real situations can be simulated using probability.
- How to allocate random numbers to events that are equally likely.
- Using random number generators such as a calculator or spreadsheet.
- Using a random device such as dice to model uniformly distributed random variables (probabilities equal).
- Using random numbers to model discrete non-uniform random variables (probabilities not equal).

Random devices

A simulation involves modelling a real situation by using the probabilities that certain outcomes will occur. Random variables are used to model probabilities. These are either uniformly distributed random variables (equal probabilities) or discrete non-uniform random variables (probabilities not equal).

A random device is a way of generating random numbers to represent the probabilities. The choice of random device often depends on the type of simulation.

Common random devices that are used in simulations are a coin or die.

Random numbers can be generated by using a calculator, spreadsheet or tables.

Once you have decided on the type of random device, you must state the rules that you will use for the simulation.

A ADVICE

Calculators have a RND button that will generate random numbers each time it is pressed. Your calculator may have a different symbol on the random number button.

EXAMPLE 1

What type of random device would you use to simulate each of these situations? State the rules of the simulation.

i) A game with two equally likely outcomes.

ii) A game with two outcomes, A with probability $\frac{1}{3}$ and B with probability $\frac{2}{3}$.

Simulation

6

SOLUTION

i) If there are two equally likely outcomes then you could use a coin. Outcome 1 would be heads and outcome 2 would be tails.

ii) If the outcomes have probabilities $\frac{1}{3}$ and $\frac{2}{3}$ then you could use a die.

The rule would be 1 and 2 represent outcome A and 3, 4, 5 and 6 represent outcome B.

A ADVICE

You could use a die for part **i)** but then the rule would be 1, 2, 3 for outcome 1 and 4, 5, 6 for outcome 2.

EXAMPLE 2

A fairground game costs £1 to play and has three possible outcomes.

- The probability of losing is $\frac{1}{6}$.
- The probability of breaking even by winning back your £1 is $\frac{1}{2}$.
- The probability of winning back your £1 plus another £1 is $\frac{1}{3}$.

Amir decides to use a die to simulate the game. What should the rules of the simulation be?

SOLUTION

One possible solution is:

	Lose £1.00	Break even	Win £1.00
Probability	$\frac{1}{6}$	$\frac{1}{2}$	$\frac{1}{3}$
	$\frac{1}{6}$	$\frac{3}{6}$	$\frac{2}{6}$
Die score	1	2, 3, 4	5, 6

A ADVICE

If the probabilities are fractions, it is a good idea to put them over a common denominator so that you can compare them easily.

A ADVICE

There are several possible correct solutions to this problem. Another possible solution would be:

	Lose £1.00	Break even	Win £1.00
Probability	$\frac{1}{6}$	$\frac{1}{2}$	$\frac{1}{3}$
	$\frac{1}{6}$	$\frac{3}{6}$	$\frac{2}{6}$
Die score	6	5, 4, 3	2, 1

EXAMPLE 3

Amir throws the die 10 times to simulate 10 tries. These are his results.

3, 5, 1, 2, 2, 3, 1, 6, 3, 6.

How much would he have won or lost if he had been really playing the game?

SOLUTION

Die score	3	5	1	2	2	3	1	6	3	6	
Winnings	0	1	−1	0	0	0	−1	1	0	1	Total = £1.00

Amir would win £1.00.

REVISE for MEI Structured Mathematics D1   65

Using random numbers

Random numbers can be used for simulation.

One-digit random numbers go from 0 to 9.

Two-digit random numbers go from 00 to 99.

It is important to set up the rules of a simulation at the beginning.

A ADVICE

You are usually asked to find an efficient rule for the simulation. This means you use as many of the available random numbers as possible.

EXAMPLE 4

In the busy lunch break, customers in a bakery have to queue. The table shows the probabilities for the queue time. Give an efficient rule using one-digit random numbers for the length of time the customers will need to queue.

Time taken (mins)	1	2	3	4
Probability	$\frac{1}{10}$	$\frac{3}{10}$	$\frac{2}{5}$	$\frac{1}{5}$

SOLUTION

A ADVICE

Sometimes an exam question will use 'RND' in tables as an abbreviation for 'Random number'.

Time taken (mins)	1	2	3	4
Probability	$\frac{1}{10}$	$\frac{3}{10}$	$\frac{2}{5}$	$\frac{1}{5}$
	$\frac{1}{10}$	$\frac{3}{10}$	$\frac{4}{10}$	$\frac{2}{10}$
Random number	0	1, 2, 3	4, 5, 6, 7	8, 9

A ADVICE

Sometimes not all random numbers are used in a simulation. There is more about this in the next section.

Running a simulation

EXAMPLE 5

Use these random numbers to simulate the waiting time for 10 customers in the bakery from Example 4. What is the average waiting time?

Random numbers, 3, 4, 4, 0, 1, 6, 9, 2, 4, 2.

SOLUTION

Customer number	Random number	Waiting time
1	3	2
2	4	3
3	4	3
4	0	1
5	1	2
6	6	3
7	9	4
8	2	2
9	4	3
10	2	2
	Total waiting time	25

Average waiting time = 25 ÷ 10 = 2.5 minutes.

EXAMPLE 6

A pair of birds can produce between two and six eggs in a clutch. The table shows the probabilities of them producing a given number of eggs, based on previous data. Give an efficient rule using two-digit random numbers to simulate the number of eggs in a clutch.

Number of eggs	2	3	4	5	6
Probability	$\frac{2}{10}$	$\frac{3}{10}$	$\frac{5}{20}$	$\frac{2}{10}$	$\frac{1}{20}$

SOLUTION

Convert all the probabilities to fractions out of 20.

$100 \div 20 = 5$ so there are 5 random numbers to represent each $\frac{1}{20}$th.

A ADVICE

Put the probabilities over a common denominator so that you can compare them easily.

Number of eggs	2	3	4	5	6
Probability	$\frac{2}{10}$	$\frac{3}{10}$	$\frac{5}{20}$	$\frac{2}{10}$	$\frac{1}{20}$
	$\frac{4}{20}$	$\frac{6}{20}$	$\frac{5}{20}$	$\frac{4}{20}$	$\frac{1}{20}$
Random number	00–19	20–49	50–74	75–94	95–99

A ADVICE

Starting at 00, allocating 20 numbers will take you to 19. The next group starts at 20 and will have 30 numbers allocated to it. To work out where it ends, add 30 to the greatest number in the previous group, so

$19 + 30 = 49$. Remember 20 is the first random number in this second group. The last number in the group is the 30th number after 19.

Now carry on like this till all the numbers have been allocated. Check your answer by making sure the allocation in the last column is correct.

LINKS

The ideas learnt in this section are essential in the next section 'Queuing simulation'.

Test Yourself ▶L

Kristof is using a die to simulate the outcomes of a game where the probability of winning is $\frac{1}{3}$, the probability of breaking even is $\frac{1}{6}$ and the probability of losing is $\frac{1}{2}$.

1 Which are the correct rules for his simulation?

A
Outcome	Win	Break even	Lose
Die score	1, 2, 3	4	5, 6

B
Outcome	Win	Break even	Lose
Die score	3	6	2

C
Outcome	Win	Break even	Lose
Die score	1, 2	3	4, 5, 6

D
Outcome	Win	Break even	Lose
Die score	1, 2	3, 4	5, 6

2 Which are the correct rules to simulate these waiting times efficiently using one-digit random numbers?

Time (mins)	1	2	3	4
Probability	$\frac{1}{10}$	$\frac{2}{5}$	$\frac{3}{10}$	$\frac{1}{5}$

A

Time (mins)	1	2	3	4
Random number	1	2, 3, 4, 5	6, 7, 8	9, 10

B

Time (mins)	1	2	3	4
Random number	0	1, 2	3, 4, 5	6

C

Time (mins)	1	2	3	4
Random number	0–9	10–39	40–79	80–99

D

Time (mins)	1	2	3	4
Random number	0	1, 2, 3, 4	5, 6, 7	8, 9

Questions 3 and 4 are about this problem.

A telesales company wants to simulate the length of calls to see whether they need to take on more staff. The lengths of calls can be modelled by this distribution.

Length of call (mins)	2–5	6–10	11–15	16–20	More than 20
Probability	$\frac{1}{4}$	$\frac{2}{5}$	$\frac{1}{5}$	$\frac{1}{10}$	$\frac{1}{20}$

3 Which are the correct rules to simulate these times efficiently using two-digit random numbers?

A

Length of call (mins)	2–5	6–10	11–15	16–20	More than 20
Random number	00–24	25–64	65–84	85–94	95–99

B

Length of call (mins)	2–5	6–10	11–15	16–20	More than 20
Random number	00–04	05–12	13–16	17–18	19

C

Length of call (mins)	2–5	6–10	11–15	16–20	More than 20
Random number	1–25	26–65	66–85	86–95	96–99

D

Length of call (mins)	2–5	6–10	11–15	16–20	More than 20
Random number	00–24	25–65	66–86	87–97	98, 99

Make sure you have the right answer to question 3 before doing question 4.

4 The simulator decides to take the mid-interval value to represent the time of the calls in each group. Use these random numbers to simulate the call time for 10 customers. What is the average call time?

Random numbers: 13, 38, 92, 65, 70, 18, 48, 63, 69, 42.

A 9.7 minutes **B** 9.6 minutes **C** 9.5 minutes **D** 10.1 minutes

Exam-Style Question

A sandwich shop calculates that 60% of its customers buy pre-packed sandwiches and 40% want their sandwiches made on the spot.

i) Give an efficient rule using one-digit random numbers to simulate the type of customer coming into the shop.

ii) Use the following random numbers to simulate the type of sandwiches bought by 10 customers. Say how many customers buy each kind of sandwich.

Random numbers: 5, 8, 2, 9, 3, 4, 7, 1, 8, 6.

Customers who want sandwiches made will have to queue to be served, then wait while their sandwich is prepared. The table shows the total length of time these customers have to wait.

Waiting time (minutes)	3	4	5	6
Probability	$\frac{1}{10}$	$\frac{1}{5}$	$\frac{2}{5}$	$\frac{3}{10}$

iii) Give an efficient rule for using two-digit random numbers to simulate the total waiting times.

iv) Use the following random numbers to simulate the waiting times for 10 customers who want their sandwiches prepared and calculate the average waiting time.

Random numbers: 23, 34, 04, 89, 61, 76, 99, 72, 27, 42.

v) Using the information from part iv), would you advise the sandwich shop owner to employ another member of staff? Give a reason for your answer.

Queuing simulation

A ABOUT THIS TOPIC

This section extends the ideas from the previous section on Monte Carlo methods, and develops longer simulations and simulations where queuing is involved.

R REMEMBER

- Basic probability from GCSE.
- The ideas from the previous section, 'Monte Carlo methods'.

K KEY FACTS

- Allocate random numbers to events correctly, to generate events with the correct probabilities.
- When probabilities are given as fractions where the denominator is not a factor of 100, adapt the rules so that some numbers are ignored.
- In a queuing simulation there are usually two variables: *inter-arrival time* and *service time*.
  - Inter-arrival time is the time between people joining a queue.
  - Service time is how long it takes to be served once a position is free.
- In a queuing simulation, time is measured from the start of the simulation.
- When variables are continuous (e.g. service time) they are usually grouped. If a calculation is needed, the mid-point is taken to give a discrete distribution.
- To improve the accuracy of a simulation, run the simulation several times.

Allocating the random numbers and ignoring some numbers

Sometimes the denominators of the probabilities do not divide exactly into 10 or 100. If a distribution does not fit exactly in to the number of possible values of random number, it is necessary to adapt rules by ignoring some numbers.

EXAMPLE 1

A factory is checking the reliability of its manufacturing process. The number of faulty items in each batch made is modelled by this distribution:

Number of faulty items	0	1	2	3
Probability	$\frac{3}{8}$	$\frac{2}{8}$	$\frac{2}{8}$	$\frac{1}{8}$

Give an efficient rule using two-digit random numbers for simulating the number of faulty items in each batch.

A ADVICE

Most questions will say **'give an efficient rule for …'**.

This means that you must use as many of the numbers as possible and must not reject more than is absolutely necessary.

Simulation

6

SOLUTION

There are 100 two-digit random numbers from 0 to 99. The probabilities are given in eighths, so first divide 100 by 8 to obtain the integer part and the remainder: $\frac{100}{8} = 12$ remainder 4.

 Simulation rules must always have a whole number of random numbers. You cannot use decimals or fractions.

This means that you will need to ignore 4 numbers and use 96 numbers ($8 \times 12 = 96$).

Number of faulty items	0	1	2	3
Probability	$\frac{3}{8}$	$\frac{2}{8}$	$\frac{2}{8}$	$\frac{1}{8}$
Random number	00–35			

The random numbers always start at 00. Twelve numbers represent each $\frac{1}{8}$. The first probability is $\frac{3}{8}$ so this will be represented by 36 numbers, 00 to 35.

Number of faulty items	0	1	2	3
Probability	$\frac{3}{8}$	$\frac{2}{8}$	$\frac{2}{8}$	$\frac{1}{8}$
Random number	00–35	36–59		

The second probability is $\frac{2}{8}$ so this will be represented by 24 numbers. Start at 36, since 35 was the greatest number used in the previous column. To work out where this group ends add the 24 to the 35, the greatest number used in the previous column.

Now complete the other two columns in the same way and state the numbers that need to be ignored.

Number of faulty items	0	1	2	3
Probability	$\frac{3}{8}$	$\frac{2}{8}$	$\frac{2}{8}$	$\frac{1}{8}$
Random number	00–35	36–59	60–83	84–95

Ignore 96, 97, 98, 99. ← You must remember to state the numbers that you are ignoring.

EXAMPLE 2

Using the simulation rules in Example 1, simulate the number of faulty items in five batches using the following random numbers.

Random numbers: 43, 67, 37, 97, 11, 86.

SOLUTION

One of the numbers is 97; this must be rejected according to the rules of the simulation.

Batch	Random number	Number of faulty items
1	43	1
2	67	2
3	37	1
4	11	0
5	86	3

Queuing simulations

Queuing simulations often come in several parts, as you can see in Example 3.

EXAMPLE 3

The following data has been collected about people arriving at a ticket office.

Inter-arrival time (minutes)	1	2	3
Probability	$\frac{1}{5}$	$\frac{1}{3}$	$\frac{7}{15}$

i) Give an efficient rule using two-digit random numbers to simulate the inter-arrival times of the customers.

ii) Use the following random numbers to simulate the inter-arrival times for 10 customers.

Random numbers: 54, 33, 92, 67, 79, 25, 53, 21, 62, 88, 52, 45, 46, 28, 81.

The time it takes to serve each customer can be modelled as:

Service time (minutes)	3	3.5	4	4.5
Probability	$\frac{1}{5}$	$\frac{1}{5}$	$\frac{1}{2}$	$\frac{1}{10}$

iii) Give an efficient rule using two-digit random numbers to simulate service times.

iv) Use the following random numbers to simulate the service times for 10 customers.

Random numbers: 17, 49, 30, 22, 62, 31, 80, 38, 16, 91, 26, 23, 34, 09, 58.

v) Use your simulated arrival times from part **ii)** and your simulated service times from part **iv)** to simulate the arrival, service and waiting time of ten customers. Find the average waiting time for the customers.

vi) What can be done to make the simulation more reliable?

SOLUTION

i)

Inter-arrival time (minutes)	1	2	3
Probability	$\frac{1}{5}$	$\frac{1}{3}$	$\frac{7}{15}$
	$\frac{3}{15}$	$\frac{5}{15}$	$\frac{7}{15}$
Random number	00–17	18–47	48–89

> Remember to put the probabilities over a common denominator so that you can compare them easily. The lowest common denominator of $\frac{1}{5}, \frac{1}{3}$ and $\frac{7}{15}$ is 15.

Ignore 90–99.

$\frac{100}{15} = 6$, remainder 10 and so there will be ten random numbers left over.

Each fifteenth uses six random numbers. Use the ninety random numbers, 00–89.

ii) Random numbers: 54, 33, 92, 67, 79, 25, 53, 21, 62, 88, 52, 45, 46, 28, 81

> ⚠ Remember to ignore 92.

Customer	Random number	Inter-arrival time
1	54	3
2	33	2
3	67	3
4	79	3
5	25	2
6	53	3
7	21	2
8	62	3
9	88	3
10	52	3

Inter-arrival time (minutes)	1	2	3
Random number	00–17	18–47	48–89

iii)

Service time (minutes)	3	3.5	4	4.5
Probability	$\frac{1}{5}$	$\frac{1}{5}$	$\frac{1}{2}$	$\frac{1}{10}$
	$\frac{2}{10}$	$\frac{2}{10}$	$\frac{5}{10}$	$\frac{1}{10}$
Random number	00–19	20–39	40–89	90–99

> Note that it is easier to allocate the random numbers for service times because the lowest common denominator of the probabilities divides exactly into 100, so all of the numbers 00–99 are allocated. There are ten random numbers for each $\frac{1}{10}$.

iv) Random numbers: 17, 49, 30, 22, 62, 31, 80, 38, 16, 91, 26, 23, 34, 09, 58.

Customer	Random number	Service time
1	17	3
2	49	4
3	30	3.5
4	22	3.5
5	62	4
6	31	3.5
7	80	4
8	38	3.5
9	16	3
10	91	4.5

Service time (minutes)	3	3.5	4	4.5
Random number	00–19	20–39	40–89	90–99

A ADVICE

If you have to do a long simulation in the exam you will usually be given a table to fill in. This will help you to understand how to organise your working.

v)

		From (ii) *Previous arrival time + inter-arrival time*	*Service starts when previous customer's service has ended*	From (iv)	*Service start + service time*	*Service start – arrival time*
Customer	**Inter arrival time**	**Arrival time**	**Service start**	**Service time**	**Service end**	**Waiting time**
1	3	3	3	3	6	0
2	2	5	6	4	10	1
3	3	8	10	3.5	13.5	2
4	3	11	13.5	3.5	17	2.5
5	2	13	17	4	21	4
6	3	16	21	3.5	24.5	5
7	2	18	24.5	4	28.5	6.5
8	3	21	28.5	3.5	32	7.5
9	3	24	32	3	35	8
10	3	27	35	4.5	39.5	8
					Total waiting time	44.5

Average waiting time $= \frac{44.5}{10} = 4.45$ minutes.

vi) To make the simulation more reliable, do more runs of the simulation.

 Service start cannot be earlier than arrival time so use arrival time for service start if previous service end is before this.

A ADVICE

If you are asked what can be done to make a simulation more reliable, you should always say run the simulation more times, since running a simulation several times will lead to more reliable results.

If you are asked for two ideas, other things that might improve the accuracy of a simulation could include:

- Do longer runs of the simulation.
- Have more accurate inter-arrival and service times, with shorter intervals between possible values. The example above uses 1, 2 or 3 as inter-arrival times. 0.5, 1, 1.5, 2, 2.5 and 3 could be used instead. The probabilities would need to be adjusted.
- Collect more data on which to base probabilities.

LINKS

It is often necessary to predict the effect of change without actually carrying out the change first. For example, changing road layouts by building roundabouts, bypasses and such things is very expensive and disruptive, so it is a good idea to first simulate the effect of the proposed change.

Simulation is used extensively in medical research, for example simulating the spread of highly contagious diseases.
Weather forecasting is an example of simulation. It uses probabilities in a very complex weather model to try to predict future weather.

Test Yourself ▶L

Questions 1 and 2 are about the following situation. Answer both questions before checking the answers.

A river ferry with space for 12 cars makes a trip every 10 minutes. Cars arrive and join the queue, crossing on the first ferry with space. The company who run the ferry decide to do a simulation to see whether it is worth buying a larger ferry.

The table below shows the inter-arrival times for cars at a busy time of day.

Arrival interval (minutes)	0.5	1	1.5	2
Probability	$\frac{1}{4}$	$\frac{3}{8}$	$\frac{1}{4}$	$\frac{1}{8}$

The company want to set up an efficient simulation using two-digit random numbers.

1 Which numbers need to be ignored?

　A none 　　　　　B 97 to 99 　　　　　C 96 to 99 　　　　　D 80 to 99

2 The rules for the simulation are formulated using two-digit random numbers. Which random numbers are allocated to the arrival interval of 1 minute?

　A 24–59 　　　　　B 25–60 　　　　　C 25–61.5 　　　　　D 20–49

3 In a queuing simulation, the rules for service times are:

Service time (minutes)	2	3	4	5
Probability	$\frac{1}{7}$	$\frac{2}{7}$	$\frac{2}{7}$	$\frac{2}{7}$

These random numbers are used to simulate the service of six customers:

　　20, 96, 60, 04, 98, 71, 32, 15.

What is the average service time for the customers?

　A $3\frac{1}{6}$ minutes 　　　B 4 minutes 　　　C $3\frac{1}{3}$ minutes 　　　D $3\frac{2}{3}$ minutes

Make sure you have the correct answer for question 3 before doing question 4.

4 In the same queuing simulation, the rules for inter-arrival times are:

Inter-arrival time (minutes)	1	2	3	4	5
Random number	00–19	20–49	50–79	80–89	90–99

These random numbers are used to simulate the inter-arrival times for the six customers whose service times have been calculated in **question 3**.

18, 42, 93, 77, 38, 87.

Use the inter-arrival times and service times to simulate six customers at the shop.
What is the average waiting time?

A $\frac{2}{3}$ minutes   **B** $1\frac{1}{2}$ minutes   **C** 9 minutes   **D** $5\frac{1}{6}$ minutes

Exam-Style Question ⊃⌐

The times Mr Green the grocer takes to serve customers have these probabilities:
2.5 minutes with probability 0.25,
3 minutes with probability 0.5,
3.5 minutes with probability 0.25.

i) Give an efficient rule for using two-digit random numbers to simulate Mr Green's service times.

ii) Use the following random numbers to simulate the service times for 10 customers.

Random numbers: 23, 34, 04, 89, 61, 76, 57, 72, 34, 42

The intervals between customers arriving at Mr Green's shop follow this distribution.

Arrival interval (minutes)	1	2	3	4
Probability	$\frac{1}{7}$	$\frac{3}{7}$	$\frac{2}{7}$	$\frac{1}{7}$

iii) Give an efficient rule for using two-digit random numbers to simulate customer arrival intervals.

iv) Use the following random numbers to simulate the inter-arrival times for 10 customers.

Random numbers: 62, 01, 99, 36, 54, 82, 89, 07, 09, 11, 50

v) Use the table below to simulate the arrival, queuing and service of 10 customers at the shop.
Use your simulated service times from part **ii)** and inter-arrival times from part **iv)**.

Customer number	Random number	Inter-arrival time	Arrival time	Service starts	Random number	Length of service	Service ends	Length of queue when customer arrives

What do you think will happen to the queue as time goes on?

vi) How could you make the simulation more reliable?

Index